D1221756

Jealott's Hill   Fifty years of Agricultural Research

Jealott's Hill

Fifty years of Agricultural Research

1928–1978

Edited by F C Peacock

ISBN 0 901747 01 7

Phototypeset in 10 on 12 point Baskerville
and printed on Paladin 115 g/m^2
at The Kynoch Press, Birmingham, England

Contents

Preface   vii

Acknowledgements   viii

1   **Introduction**   1–9

F C Peacock

2   **Crop nutrition and management**   10–28

E R Armitage, A E M Hood, E R Dinnis, S W Hawkins,
H Lidgate, T R Owen, W Thompson

3   **Seed treatments**   29–34

M R Middleton, R Cotterell, J E Elsworth, D A Harris,
D Price Jones, L S Lloyd

4   **Selective herbicides**   35–41

H P Allen, R C Brian, J E Downes, G C Mees, R H Springett

5   **Benzene hexachloride**   42–48

J F Newman, F L C Baranyovits, H R Jameson, D Price Jones

6   **Organophosphorus insecticides**   49–54

A Calderbank

7   **The gibberellins**   55–60

G C Mees, G W Elson

8 **Taking stock**   61–66

J T Braunholtz

9 **Bipyridylium herbicides**   67–86

A Calderbank, R C Brian, H P Allen, G Douglas,
D W R Headford, R S L Jeater, R H Springett, A F J Wheeler

10 **Pyrimidine fungicides**   87–97

K J Bent, D H Brooks, R S Elias, J R Finney,
Claire Shephard, B K Snell

11 **Pyrimidine insecticides**   98–109

B K Snell, F L C Baranyovits, N D Bishop, G C Mees,
J H Proctor

12 **Involvement overseas**   110–118

I E Darter, R S Elias, R E Plowman

13 **Environmental studies**   119–128

R J Hemingway, J F Newman

14 **'Unsuccessful' ventures**   129–136

R C Brian, P F H Freeman, H R Jameson, F C Peacock

15 **Single-cell protein**   137–144

N Watchorn, J F Matthews, A E Rout

16 **Perspective**   145–148

J T Braunholtz

Indexes   149–160

Preface

The compilation of this history of ICI's research at Jealott's Hill presented certain editorial problems. Some of the work described came to an end years ago and is now properly historical. Some, notably that of long-term agronomic concern, has been continuous over the whole period. Much of the remainder is relatively recent and is not yet concluded. The book takes the form of a series of technical chapters linked, tenuously, by a narrative thread, and this necessarily involves some overlapping, both within and between chapters, and changes of tense from the past to the present.

Scientific terminology also has changed over the fifty-year period; this applies to chemical nomenclature and particularly to units of measurement. In this book historic usage has been followed, but wherever appropriate, and at least on first mention, present-day equivalents have also been given.

There are many names in the book which will be familiar to only a few specialists outside Jealott's Hill. But the strength of a research station lies in the people who work there; hence, credit has been given where possible to those who could readily be identified with particular phases of the work. Unfortunately, many hundreds more, who contributed ideas and the essential back-up services without which no discovery could be translated into a commercial success, have had to be omitted. Their efforts nevertheless were appreciated, and are gratefully acknowledged. For the benefit of those readers concerned with editorial consistency, the rationale adopted in the technical chapters has been to give initials (but no title) on first mention; initials are omitted thereafter, unless the name recurs at some distance from the first mention or is listed in a group which includes names mentioned for the first time.

Editorial conservatism and the remnants of chivalry dictated exceptions in the case of titled and honoured names, and lady members of staff.

The technical chapters were drafted by working parties consisting of existing and recently retired Jealott's Hill staff who either were themselves concerned with, or could be expected to remember details of, the work, with recourse to published and internal Company reports.

Acknowledgements

Parentage of the chapters is acknowledged in the table of contents, where chapter co-ordinators are shown in bold type. Certain sources of material must also be acknowledged. The historical introduction, for example, drew on ICI records, notes by E R Armitage and D J Halliday and published accounts by Sir William Gavin, D Price Jones, George Ordish and W J Reader. In the selective herbicide chapter reference was made to reports and publications by W G Templeman, a published account by I M Burnet and an unpublished manuscript by Celia Kirby. The BHC story drew on an unpublished account by C C Tanner and published histories by George Ordish and W J Reader. The involvement of Machinery Development Group is spread over many chapters; accounts were contributed by A Bloomfield and J E Elsworth. Photographs, unless otherwise acknowledged, were taken by ICI staff; the line drawings were the work of Anne Fincher.

Originally, it was thought that the bones of scientific research might be clothed with humorous anecdotage, and material almost sufficient for another book was contributed by J L and Kay Charlton, G H and Joyce Stock, S J Lamden, A Wise, E R Armitage, E Callan and M V Thruston. Regrettably, as the book developed, this was seen to be inappropriate and of little interest outside Jealott's Hill; but it is mentioned here because such 'in-house' humour is believed to be the leavening in the mixture that goes to make a successful research team.

On points of historical detail, frequent recourse was made to the memories of C Campbell, Olive Nichols and Florence Piper.

The Editorial Board of *Outlook on Agriculture* consisting of J T Braunholtz (Chairman), H P Allen, A Calderbank, I E Darter, P Doyle, N Watchorn and T I Williams read the chapters critically and made many valuable suggestions. The final manuscript also embodies the comments of C H Reece and W Johnstone, the Chairman and Deputy Chairman of ICI Plant Protection Division respectively and of P King and D S Hay of ICI Agricultural Division. Thanks are also due to W R Boon, G Watts Padwick, C C Tanner and S W Cheveley, for reading the manuscript and offering the invaluable guidance that only their personal involvement in much of what is recorded here could provide.

The manuscripts were typed, many times, and the proofs read by Gwen Hardwidge, whose wise counsel also restrained the number of editorial irrelevancies appearing in print.

Chapter 1

Introduction

Commemoration of a Golden Jubilee needs to be tempered with modesty, or it may appear presumptuous to those who have already celebrated the occasion, and patronising to those who have not yet earned such a right. However, the past fifty years have seen astonishing developments in agricultural research and its application to farming practice and, in many of these, Jealott's Hill has played a leading role. A certain pride in achievement, therefore, may perhaps be forgiven; and it is a fact that, free of the tyranny of the Annual Report, Jealott's Hill's activities have not before been published, except in scattered scientific memoranda and the technical literature of the commercially successful end-products. This commemorative book, then, is both an introduction to, and an account of ICI, Jealott's Hill: its objectives, successes and failures; and of the people who work there, many of whom may, themselves, be ill-informed as to what has gone before.

The name Jealott's Hill appears to have derived from Roger *alias* Jolyf, a Berkshire landowner during the reign of Henry IV. Two centuries later, in 1606, the area was common land and known as Joyliff's Hill. Subsequently this became Jealous Hill, for Thomas Hearne (1678–1735), describing the perambulation of the bounds of White Waltham, wrote: ". . . taking in a small cottage with an orchard, they pass on to Tutchin-lane-end . . . turn southward and pass by Bray Wood side, 'till they come near the great pond, where there is a very large stone fix'd deep in the ground, call'ed Red Stone. Leaving this stone they turn westward, 'till they come quite to the bottom of Jealous Hill . . . '. Roque's *Topographical Survey of the County of Berks,* dated 1761, shows the farm, its boundaries differing little from those of today, but no name is given. Jealous Hill appears again on H Walter's *Map of Windsor Forest,* 1823 and was owned by Lord Braybrooke of Billingbere. The first record of the name 'Jealots' Hill is on John Snares' map, dated 1846.

At about this time, J B Lawes and J H Gilbert were conducting their experiments with various manurial treatments including 'artificial' fertilizers, at Rothamsted in Hertfordshire, and the Royal Agricultural College at

Cirencester had just been founded. The widespread interest in agricultural experimentation thus generated led to the setting-up of a number of privately or co-operatively-financed Research Stations such as Woburn (1894), Long Ashton (1902), East Malling (1913), Cheshunt (1914) and the first commercial agricultural research laboratory, by William Cooper of Berkhamsted in 1902; though the latter was concerned primarily with animal health problems, such as 'footrot' of sheep, for which cresol, arsenic and copper sulphate dips were widely used. In this business Cooper was in competition with McDougall of Manchester and Robertson of Oban. The realisation that copper compounds were general fungicides and, particularly, that they were effective against potato blight *(Phytophthora infestans)*, brought Cooper into the crop protection field; the recognition of the aphicidal properties of soap brought in, among others, Abol Ltd ('abol'-ish aphids) and the Yalding Manufacturing Co., local companies supplying the fruit and hop growers of Kent.

The discovery, shortly after the first World War, that derris, of proven efficacy as a sheep dip, also controlled aphids and caterpillars, interested McDougall Bros in crop protection and, by a series of amalgamations, the firms of McDougall & Robertson, Cooper & Nephews, McDougall & Yalding and Abol Ltd merged to form, in 1927, Cooper, McDougall & Robertson Ltd.

But this digresses from the story of Jealott's Hill, which in the meantime had acquired its present spelling.

By 1923 the firm of Brunner, Mond had successfully translated its version of the Haber-Bosch high-pressure ammonia process into a commercial operation at Billingham on Teesside; and with the formation, in 1926, of Imperial Chemical Industries Ltd, in which Brunner, Mond was merged, the chemical industry was about to embark upon a massive programme of capital expenditure and expansion in fertilizer manufacture.

Nitram Ltd was the selling agent for the British Sulphate of Ammonia Federation (non-ICI), and Synthetic Ammonia and Nitrates Ltd (a Brunner, Mond subsidiary), and already had a team of qualified agricultural advisers who, in addition to field advisory work, produced leaflets and sales literature including a widely-circulated journal *Farm Notes on Profitable Farming.*

In June 1927 Nitram Ltd bought the adjoining farms of Jealott's Hill, Hawthorndale and Nuptown, together some 433 acres, near Bracknell in Berkshire, to serve as a centre for agricultural research and demonstration. The initial objective was to popularise the use, by the farmers of Great Britain and the Empire, of nitrogen on grass, and to encourage the adoption of the 'Intensive system of grassland management' by which, it was confidently claimed, the stock-carrying capacity of pastures could be greatly increased.

Sir Alfred Mond (later Lord Melchett), the first Chairman of ICI, was determined that his new Company should be supported by both pure and applied research, and had persuaded Sir Frederick Keeble FRS, then Sherardian Professor of Botany at Oxford, to join ICI 'to devote himself to Research and Propaganda in Fertilizers". The term 'propaganda' had not yet acquired its pejorative connotation.

On ICI's take-over of Nitram Ltd in 1929 Sir Frederick became the first Director of the ICI Agricultural Research Station, Jealott's Hill, with T H J Carroll of Nitram as Deputy Director. The offical opening on 28 June 1929, belied the fact that field experiments had been going on throughout 1928, conducted by staff housed in two old army huts while more permanent quarters were being built. Some idea of the extent of these activities is given

Jealott's Hill 1928. Headquarters building

by the Programme of Arrangements, Exhibits and Demonstrations produced at the offical opening. The 700 guests, after a welcome and address by the Rt Hon J H Thomas, Lord Privy Seal, followed by lunch, were invited to inspect the laboratories, greenhouses, offices and library, and to see demonstrations of grass preservation, with two types of experimental grass-drying plant and various dried-grass products; Intensive Grassland Management, exemplified by comparative studies of milk production, sheep, pig and baby beef rearing systems; experiments on the manuring of barley, oats, sugar beet, potatoes and wheat; and deep cultivation with steam tackle.

The senior research staff at this time included H J Page (Chief Chemist), S J Watson (Animal Nutrition), A H Lewis (Soils & Fertilizers), A W Greenhill (Analytical), G E Blackman (Botanist) and J Procter (Field Experiments). M S Bartlett was the Statistician and Kathleen Sinclair was Librarian. In August of the same year the adjoining Hawthorndale estate was purchased; this consisted of a sixteen-bedroomed mansion which was to be used as a club and guest house, and a further 100 acres of land. By 1930, staff numbered 99 'including 36 research and experimental staff and 8 trainees'.

It is interesting to note, in the light of present-day values, that the original laboratory cost £15,000; capital outlay by May 1930 was put at £103,785 and the Jealott's Hill budget for that year was £50,000. But then, the purchase of the farm, together with live and dead stock, had involved little more than £19,000.

It is also salutary to recall Keeble's definition of the basic principles by which alone, in his view, a commercially-financed research station could maintain a reputation for integrity comparable to that of university and independent research centres. 'It must be the guide', he said, 'and not the servant of the Company; it must be free to publish all results; its quest must be knowledge, not sales; its unswerving aim the long-term prosperity of Agriculture irrespective of the immediate interests of the Company, since, in the long run, both are identical. As a corollary to this, it must be free to embark on fundamental research showing no prospect of immediate gain. Only on this basis,' said Sir Frederick, 'can I attract the men I want and keep their enthusiasm.'

Fifty years later it must be conceded that 'the freedom to publish all results' has been eroded to some extent by Official Secrets Acts, Home Office edicts and Patent Law, in university and in industry alike. The pursuit of knowledge for its own sake has likewise been tempered to the wind of commerce, but integrity of research and the long-term prosperity of Agriculture remain the aims, as unswerving now as then.

It is not the intention of this book to eulogize the commercial successes for which Jealott's Hill and ICI are known, but to record with historical accuracy, and as objectively as human nature will allow, the Station's involvement in agricultural research over a half-century of very considerable technological change. Thus, the reader will find accounts of research which led nowhere; research which might have had much greater impact than, in the event, it did; research which had a successful outcome, in the long run, against all probability; and long-term research whose 'success' it is impossible to estimate in commercial terms, but which is a source of interest, and hopefully, inspiration, to thousands of farmers and others who visit Jealott's Hill each year.

It often seems that 'success' is due to the chance combination of 'the right man in the right place at the right time', but the creation of an intellectual atmosphere such as that at Jealott's Hill, which allows the time and the place to produce the man, must be accountable.

The story of over-optimistic estimates of fertilizer sales, against the background of the steadily worsening world economic depression of the 1920s, and the measures taken to reduce production at Billingham, has been told in detail in W J Reader's history of ICI [1]. At Jealott's Hill in 1931 Keeble's budget was halved. Staff numbers were reduced and those who remained, in common with senior staff throughout ICI, took a 10% cut in salary, though for weekly-paid workers it was only 5%. Salaries were restored by April 1933, but Keeble retired at the end of 1932, as Reader says 'no doubt bitterly disappointed', and was succeeded by H J Page with the title of 'Controller' of Research.

Although Billingham remained a depressed area, with half the fertilizer plant closed down, trade in other Divisions of ICI recovered more rapidly and the Company began to develop its interests in pesticides. Dyestuffs and General Chemicals Division had been involved for some years, Dyestuffs with fungicidal seed dressings, General Chemicals with arsenicals and cyanide fumigation. In 1936, Page was appointed Director of the Rubber Research Institute of Malaya, to be succeeded by S J Watson as Controller at Jealott's Hill. A new unit, known as the Hawthorndale Biological Laboratories, was formed under the direction of a Pest Control Research Committee drawn from the joint research departments of Dyestuffs and General Chemicals Divisions, and directed by W V Blewett.

So began an administrative split which was not always in the best interests of efficient running of the Station. Hawthorndale, with O B Lean as its Head and Chief Entomologist and R C Woodward as Chief Mycologist, was mainly concerned with the biological evaluation of chemicals from Dyestuffs at Blackley and General Chemicals at Runcorn. Jealott's Hill pursued its longer-term and less overtly commercially-oriented work on grassland management (Martin Jones), soils and fertilizers (A H Lewis), animal nutrition (W S Ferguson), and plant physiology (G E Blackman and W G Templeman) under the direction of S J Watson, each sub-Station responding independently to an Agricultural Committee (W V Blewett, R E Slade and Col W R Peel) but having a common local administration variously under B A Fixsen and A P Allan.

ICI's growing interests in the field of crop protection now began to conflict with those of Cooper, McDougall & Robertson and in June 1937 a joint company, Plant Protection Ltd, was formed; curiously, the share capital was '£1900 divided into 1900 shares of £1 each'. The new company had offices in London, but the technical staff were based at Yalding in Kent. ICI contributed the research facilities at Jealott's Hill and took over the manufacturing side, including the factory at Yalding; Coopers provided the commercial and distributive expertise. (For a variety of reasons this proved to be a somewhat inharmonious alliance, particularly in research liaison; Plant Protection, after all, had its own technical staff, with a better knowledge of the market than ICI. But it worked tolerably well in practice and lasted until 1958, when ICI bought out the crop protection interests of Cooper, McDougall & Robertson, and Plant Protection Ltd became a wholly-owned ICI subsidiary).

By 1938, war with Germany had become virtually certain and plans for increasing Britain's self-sufficiency in food were well advanced. ICI had pioneered intensive and extended grass production with campaigns for 'early bite' and 'late bite' using nitrogenous and 'Concentrated Complete Fertilizers', and grass drying. In 1938 Slade, who was now ICI Research Controller, initiated work at Jealott's Hill on the caustic soda treatment of straw to give the carbohydrate balance for the protein-rich diet that would be provided by dried-grass products. In the event, grass-drying never really 'caught on' as a conservation process on the farm, though there was a great deal of interest in it after the war. Silage, which had also been a feature of Jealott's Hill research and which in 1940 ICI was strongly advocating in the 'corridors of power'—the Agricultural Research Council and the Ministry of

Agriculture—did, with a campaign to provide a million tons of silage, run by the county War Agricultural Executive Committees, relying heavily on help from ICI and training at Jealott's Hill. Sir William Gavin, then ICI's Agricultural Adviser, became Chief Agricultural Adviser to the Ministry of Agriculture. Watson was co-opted onto the Ministry Scientific Advisory Panel on Feed Production, and with Col Peel onto the government Grassland Improvement Committee. S W Cheveley, who had been Secretary of Nitram Ltd and hence closely involved both with the purchase and the early running of Jealott's Hill, joined Gavin and Sir George Stapledon on the Ministry's Technical Development Committee to help run 'a general campaign for the improvement and fuller use of grass' alongside the silage campaign.

With the National Emergency of World War II and the need to 'Grow More Food', to quote a poster of the times, Jealott's Hill attained the status and reputation Keeble had hoped for.

On the face of it, the war years were a quiet time at Jealott's Hill. A Local Defence Volunteer (later known as the Home Guard) unit was formed, and staff took their turn at 'fire-watching'. One November night in 1940 five bombs fell in Jealott's Hill fields, but it is believed that this event was accidental, and that the enemy High Command was never advised of the importance of Jealott's Hill as a target!

But, strangely, bereft of administrative re-organization for 'the duration' Jealott's Hill and Hawthorndale each produced one of the most significant discoveries in their separate or combined history, or indeed, in the history of crop protection. W G Templeman's observation, in 1940, of the astonishingly selective herbicidal activity of α-naphthylacetic acid and the subsequent synthesis, selection and development of 2,4-D and MCPA revolutionised weed control in cereals; whilst at Hawthorndale the re-discovery in 1942 of the insecticidal properties of benzene hexachloride, and in particular its gamma isomer, by F J D Thomas and H R Jameson, shared with DDT credit for the dawn of a new era of insect control in agriculture, horticulture, stored products, timber preservation and public health. Effective locust control became a practicality and O B Lean was seconded to Locust Control, Middle East, leaving Woodward in charge of Hawthorndale, until the appointment in 1944 of C C Tanner who, with J C Smart, L J Burrage and others, had been working on the chemical problems of BHC in the research laboratories of General Chemicals Division. Watson was appointed to the Chair of Agriculture at Edinburgh and was succeeded by Lewis, he and Tanner responding independently to a new Central Agricultural Control under the Chairmanship of F C O Speyer, another ex-Nitram man.

These war-time years saw the development of selective herbicides (not solely by Jealott's Hill, as a later chapter will make clear), BHC—which was so effective against the initial target pest, flea beetle (*Phyllotreta* spp) that this is now no longer regarded as being of economic importance in Britain, and dual-purpose BHC/organomercurial seed dressings which relegated wireworms (*Agriotes lineatus*) as a pest of cereals to much the same status. The remarkable activity of the new chemicals at low dosage called for new means of applying them, and the first low-volume sprayer in Britain was developed at Jealott's Hill. Remote from these stirring practical developments a small unit under P W Brian was laying the foundations for what was to become, on its move to Welwyn in 1955, and until its dissolution in 1964, the more academic Akers Laboratories. This non-Divisional research establishment carried out fundamental studies in natural science and produced, apart from intangible benefits in terms of ICI expertise, the antibiotic griseofulvin, gibberellic acid fermentation technology, four Professors, two Readers and a Director of a National Research Institute.

On the return to peace-time conditions, Plant Protection Ltd in 1945 purchased the Verdley Estate of some 400 acres at Fernhurst in Sussex. The history of 'Fernhurst' as it has become widely known, is another story; its crop management, however, brought to the notice of Jealott's Hill, and ICI, the existence of other branches of farming—fruit, hops and horticulture; no revelation to Plant Protection Ltd, which, as has been shown, grew up in the 'Garden of England', but a considerable departure from ICI's hitherto 'broad acres' interests.

It would be splendid, though possibly tedious, to be able to recount an unbroken succession of discoveries turned to brilliant account, but history dictates otherwise. As in a military campaign where advances must be consolidated, bases supplied and armies re-grouped, ICI's crop protection ventures needed a breathing-space. With the return to a commercially competitive atmosphere, and with several major products whose acceptance into agricultural practice produced a host of technical service problems, another 'break-through' might well have proved an embarrassment. Jealott's Hill re-trenched and kept, in current jargon, 'a low profile' for the next fifteen years. A Farm Advisory Service was initiated; a Farm Economics Section, which carried out full costings on selected representative farms, a training unit for agricultural development officers, and, with the appointment of P A Collier, a Statistics Section, came into being. Staff, and laboratory space, increased. The Library, quite properly the fulcrum of the 1928 Jealott's Hill, became an Intelligence Section with the appointment of Evelyn Attwood and D J Halliday, and produced some classic monographs [2] [3].

Chemistry, hitherto something which went on in the remote Midlands and Northern Divisions, arrived, in the shape of a concrete-mixer for formulating field-experiment quantities of experimental compounds, and a resident experienced Works Chemist, F L Sharp, who, incidentally, inculcated the rudiments of a 'safety in handling' code upon a band of enthusiasts who went happily about their work reeking of whatever chemical they happened to be involved with.

The post-war revelation of the development of organophosphorus insecticide chemistry by Schrader and co-workers in Germany had been received with less than unqualified enthusiasm in ICI; the compounds were 'too toxic' and anyway there was 'little room for further discovery'. The belated recognition that this was an opinion not shared by other chemical companies coincided with the formation at Jealott's Hill in 1954 of a Synthetic Chemistry section, drawn from the research department of Dyestuffs Division, under the direction of W R Boon, who came to share with Templeman the role of Associate Research Director under Lewis.

This period of quiescence was characterised by innumerable administrative changes, by considerable expansion in existing areas of synthetic and formulation chemistry and by the creation of new biochemical, analytical and physical chemistry groups. It was a buoyant period, during which ICI's sales of fertilizers, selective herbicides and dual-purpose seed dressings paid for more academic activities such as studies of chemical structure/activity relationships, protein from unicellular algae, and insect physiology. And it came to an end with the realization, on ICI's acquisition in 1958 of Cooper, McDougall & Robertson's crop protection interests, of the extent to which the manufacturing Divisions of ICI had been subsidising the crop protection business. The ensuing re-structuring of the now wholly ICI-owned Plant Protection Ltd led, in 1959, to redundancies and some bitterness and tarnished the Company's benign image. Believing, like Macbeth, that 'if it were done when 'tis done, then 'twere well it were done quickly' the Company lost weight overnight. It had to. Cuts were heaviest at Fernhurst, but Jealott's Hill also felt the wind. Central Agricultural Control was wound up. The crop production and crop protection sides of Jealott's Hill at last came together when, in 1964, Plant Protection Ltd and the Billingham Group became Agricultural Division. A leaner organisation moved on into the 1960s and the next fifteen years was to be the most productive period so far, though many of the ideas to be developed had in fact already been conceived.

Synthetic chemical work in the organophosphorus field by R Ghosh and others had already produced amiton (1952), later abandoned because of high toxicity, and menazon (1958) the first truly specific and environmentally acceptable aphicide.

A relatively brief excursion into carbamate chemistry produced pirimicarb (1965) whilst the longer-term involvement with related pyrimidine phosphorus chemistry resulted in the selection of pirimiphos-ethyl (1965) and pirimiphos-methyl (1967), insecticides of more general application. Similarly, P W Brian and S H Crowdy's work on systemic fungicides in the 1950s may be seen to have paved the way, certainly in terms of the development of technique, for the discovery in the 1960s of the remarkable systemic fungicidal properties of the pyrimidines, and the development, for mildew control, of dimethirimol on cucurbits (1965) ethirimol on cereals (1966), and bupirimate on apples (1969).

But undoubtedly, the conspicuous success which characterised this period, dominated the efforts of Jealott's Hill and Fernhurst, and changed the farming scene, was the discovery of the unique herbicidal properties of the bipyridylium cations diquat and paraquat; even more significant was the recognition of how these properties could be turned to the advantage of farmers the world over. The initial discovery, in 1955, was the result of close co-operation between a team of chemists at Dyestuffs Division and R F Homer and R C Brian at Jealott's Hill. But the architect of the successful development of diquat and paraquat was assuredly W R Boon, who as chemist, Director of Jealott's Hill (which he became on Lewis's retirement in 1964) R & D Director and finally, joint Managing Director of Plant

Protection Ltd, was personally and totally committed to what he regarded as the most significant development in agriculture since the introduction of the wheeled plough.

On Boon's appointment as Joint Managing Director of Plant Protection Ltd in 1969, J T Braunholtz assumed responsibility for the research and development direction of an organisation which, in the space of ten years, had become a major presence in international crop protection, and which in 1975 attained the status of an ICI Division.

Braunholtz's direction was to last until 1977 when he became Product & Planning Director, to be succeeded at Jealott's Hill by P Doyle from Pharmaceuticals Division. The crop production and animal nutrition groups at Jealott's Hill remained, appropriately, a part of Agricultural Division, having close ties with Billingham, which, after all, is where it all started, fifty years ago.

So it is logical that the first technical chapter of this book should return the reader to fertilizers, and grass, and the beginnings of research at Jealott's Hill.

References

[1] Reader W J (1975) *Imperial Chemical Industries: a history.* Vol. 2. *The first quarter-century 1926–1952.* Oxford University Press. pp. xvii+569.

[2] Halliday D J (1948) *A guide to the uptake of plant nutrients by farm crops.* Jealott's Hill Bulletin No 7 (reprinted 1948).

[3] Halliday D J, Sylvester J B (1950) *Nitrogen for grass. A survey of the response of grass to nitrogen fertilizers.* Jealott's Hill Bulletin No 9.

Hawthorndale built 1880. Acquired 1929

Chapter 2

Crop nutrition and management

Many of the problems that Jealott's Hill began to study in the 1920s have continued to be of interest to the present day. This is hardly surprising, for no two seasons are alike, and the environmental make-up of each field is unique. In agriculture there can be no single formula for success; improvements depend upon a background of scientific observation, and evolve slowly and painstakingly from experience.

Historically and commercially it was natural that the attention of the ICI soil chemists and agronomists should first be directed to the effect of fertilizers, and particularly nitrogen fertilizers, on crop growth; but, from the beginning, the principles of good husbandry dictated that they should examine the influence of ICI's products on farm practices as well as on the crops themselves. Grass, a crop peculiarly suited to the climate of the British Isles, is also particularly responsive to nitrogen fertilizers; so Jealott's Hill then, as now, was concerned with grassland management. Grass, however, is basically a summer crop and its preservation without loss of nutritional qualities poses problems: hence an interest in forage conservation that has been maintained throughout fifty years of experimentation at Jealott's Hill.

Such were the recurrent themes that were to form the subjects of research; the physical resources for the investigations were at first the fields, laboratories and greenhouses at Jealott's Hill but these were later augmented by the purchase of a number of 'development' farms when, in 1944, ICI set up a unique Division known as Central Agricultural Control (CAC) charged with the responsibility for all the Company's research & development activities in the agricultural sphere. From then until it was wound up in 1958, CAC, under the chairmanship first of F C O Speyer and then of S W Cheveley, involved ICI ever increasingly and effectively in the practical business of farming. It acquired three farms down the western side of the country with the specific purpose of examining the problems of intensive fertilizer use on grass, and it appointed R A Hamilton, recruited from the N Ireland Ministry of Agriculture, to be Development Director.

The three farms were The Leaths, Castle Douglas, Kirkcudbrightshire (a 500-acre mixed crop and livestock farm on light stony ground in SW Scotland), Dairy House, Middlewich (a 400-acre flat dairy farm on the Cheshire clay plain), and Henley Manor (a 440-acre farm at Crewkerne in Somerset, with very variable soils ranging from medium to heavy loams to sands, brash and limestone). Overall responsibility for management rested initially with O J Pattison, then with R R Turner and, after 1968, W Thompson.

The dominant interest at Henley Manor and Dairy House had always been in dairying but in 1964 the Division widened its interests by acquiring a 1400-acre farm at Wilton in Cleveland. The land at Wilton stretched from good lowland arable up the side of the Cleveland Hills and it was decided to make this a focal centre for ICI's growing concern with meat production systems.

In 1968 Wilton was opened as a development farm and two years later The Leaths was sold, since ICI's interest in fertilizer promotion work in Scotland had passed to its subsidiary, Scottish Agricultural Industries. At about the same time the Jealott's Hill farm was incorporated within the Group so that the land and livestock not occupied by experiments could be used for fertilizer development work of the same nature as that at the other farms.

The Farmhouse, Jealott's Hill

To complete the account, mention should be made of a further farm at Saltholme in the heavily industrialised area north of the Tees estuary and adjacent to the ICI Billingham plant. This farm of 2600 acres carries a herd of 400 single-suckler beef cows and 1100 breeding ewes, fattening all the progeny. It also grows over 800 acres of cereals. Although it is used to a small extent for ICI development work on fertilizer spreading and handling methods, fertilizer storage trials, livestock trials and silage-making techniques, it is farmed essentially as a commercial venture and is not open to the public.

Nitrogen and Crop Growth

For a long time, fertilizer nitrogen was considered to be harmful to grassland because it apparently suppressed clovers; but, even before the establishment of Jealott's Hill, the forerunners of ICI had been interested in the use of nitrogen on pastures. In the autumn of 1925, T H J Carroll and S W Cheveley of Nitram Limited (the nitrogen-fertilizer marketing subsidiary of Brunner Mond & Co Ltd) had set up the first farm demonstration of the 'New System of Grassland Management' at Marton-in-Cleveland, and plans were in hand for a series of demonstrations throughout the British Isles. Some farms were already using the system of paddock grazing with application of fertilizers (particularly nitrogen), that had been developed at Hohenheim in Germany, and when the ICI Agricultural Research Station was founded at Jealott's Hill, this system was investigated on Leakes Meadow by A W Greenhill [1], H J Page and S J Watson over the period 1929–1934. Although the system was referred to as the 'Intensive System of Grassland Management' the level of nitrogen manuring, which averaged about 70 lb N/acre each year, would hardly, by modern standards, be considered to be intensive. The experiment showed, however, that not only were extra dry-matter and crude protein always obtained from the use of fertilizer N, but a more even growth of grass occurred over the season.

At the same time, Martin Jones was demonstrating, in a classic experiment in Drownboy Field, the importance of sward management in grassland production [2]. He showed that hard spring grazing by sheep encouraged clover growth in a mixed sward, while lighter grazing increased productivity from the grass. When the system incorporated overgrazing in the early spring and undergrazing in mid-season, however, grassy and broad-leaved weeds, especially thistles, tended to take over.

The effect of nitrogen fertilizer on the extension of the grazing season and on the production of an even growth was also studied. During the years 1930–1934 G E Blackman carried out a series of trials from which he concluded that below a soil temperature of 40°F (5·0°C) growth of grass was inhibited, but that over a temperature range of 42–49°F (5·5–9·5°C) soil nitrogen nitrified slowly and growth could be increased by applying nitrogen fertilizer. By suitable grazing management and the application of nitrogen in February or March, sufficient growth could generally be obtained to feed cattle on pasture about two weeks earlier than usual, for which the term 'early bite' was coined. Using a calcium bentonite/sand mixture of low microbial activity in pot culture, A H Lewis demonstrated that, while grass could take up nitrogen in both ammoniacal and nitrate forms, for early growth the ammoniacal form was the more efficient. Later, consideration of factors involved in a field situation led to the favouring of the 'dual-purpose' ammonium nitrate.

In a series of field experiments, Blackman and W G Templeman showed, by shading plots of a mixed grass/clover sward with muslin, that there was a marked inter-relationship between light intensity and nitrogen effects, and they concluded that the battle between legumes and grasses depended largely upon competition for light [3]. Since both density and height of grasses depend on nitrogen supply, additional nitrogen may depress legume growth merely by increasing the degree of shading.

Rotations and Soil Fertility

In 1945 A E M Hood and J Procter began two long-term experiments to investigate the effects of cropping sequences on crop yields and soil fertility; these experiments each lasted twelve years. In one, a study was made of intensive cereal growing, comparing continuous culture with one year 'breaks' of ley (either grazed or cut for hay), rape (grazed), mustard (as green manure), and bare fallow. The test crops, in sequence, were winter wheat, spring oats and spring barley.

Results were quite unequivocal and showed that yields of wheat following leys increased with time, whereas yields on the other rotations, especially continuous cereals, declined [4].

In the second experiment the effects of one-, two-, and three-year leys on crop yields and soil characteristics were measured alongside an all-arable rotation. These studies clearly indicated the value of leys under Jealott's Hill conditions (where the soil is derived from Plateau Gravel overlying London Clay). Crop yields following continuous-cereal or -arable culture were reduced by a greater incidence of take-all disease *(Ophiobolus graminis)* in winter wheat, more grass weeds, and by deterioration of the soil structure, which reduced the 'workability' of the soil and made it slower to dry out in the spring.

Such observations in the field were confirmed by laboratory tests devised by A J Low to assess the stability of the soil aggregates under the different farming systems; and, by extending this work to soils from many parts of England, Low highlighted the differences associated with long periods under either grassland or arable husbandry. Old grassland soils contained more organic matter, more total pore space, and aggregates of greater water stability [5].

Subsidiary treatments in the field experiments showed that different methods of straw disposal (removed, burned or ploughed in) had negligible effects either on crop yields or on soil structure. Farmyard manure, applied one year in five, showed a modest yield increase in the year of application to kale in the ley rotations but none in the all-arable systems.

Grass

Over the years, many trials were carried out on a range of grass varieties using nitrogen rates up to and beyond 800 units N/acre per annum. (Units of N was a system, devised by G W Cooke at Rothamsted, which is no longer used; 1 unit of N/acre was equivalent to 1·12 lb/ac or 1·25 kg/ha). The yields obtained varied with weather and sward but generally increased linearly up to 250–300 units N/acre, at which point the average yield was about 5·5 tons dry-matter/acre. Maximum yields were obtained using some 400 units/acre when, in one season, almost 8 tons of dry-matter/acre were harvested.

The importance of applying nitrogen immediately after cutting was demonstrated in two series of trials carried out between 1950 and 1968 when fertilizer nitrogen, up to an annual total of 940 kg N/ha, was given in split applications to grass both for drying and for silage, either immediately after cutting or after an interval of 14 days. Although the quality of the herbage, in terms of crude protein content, was better from the later application, total grass yields were invariably higher when nitrogen was applied immediately after cutting.

Since the beginning of the present decade the effects of very heavy dressings of nitrogen have been compared on both well-established and newer varieties of grasses, especially ryegrasses (early, medium and late perennials, Italian, hybrid and tetraploid varieties). Grass/clover mixtures with both red and white clovers have also been included. In a fixed-site trial from 1971–1974, one variety, Melle, a late perennial ryegrass which responded to nitrogen up to 640 kg/ha, consistently outyielded six other varieties in the trial by a margin of about 20%. Under summer drought conditions in 1975 and 1976, however, yields from Melle were not outstanding.

Mixed Grass/Clover Swards

New strains of clover developed by the Welsh Plant Breeding Station increased the potential contribution of clovers both to herbage production and to cereals in a ley system of farming, and considerable work was carried out, both at Jealott's Hill and on ICI farms, to measure the contribution of clover to herbage production. It had been established that the addition of nitrogen fertilizers to a mixed sward increased the growth of grass and, as a result of competition, the clover content declined.

In 1950, Hood started a series of trials at Jealott's Hill to compare all-grass swards receiving nitrogen fertilizer, at rates up to 450 lb N/acre/ annum, with grass/clover plots receiving no nitrogen fertilizer. The yield of dried herbage from the grass/clover was, in general, similar to that from all-grass plots receiving about 150 lb N/acre/annum. Maximum production from any sward however, required about 450 lb N/acre.

Between 1956 and 1961 nine long-term experiments were conducted by E R Armitage at Henley Manor Farm in Somerset, where clovers grew prolifically in mixed swards. While the yield from the unfertilized grass/clover was high (3·75 tons/acre), that obtained by the use of heavy dressings of nitrogen was considerably greater (5·5 tons/acre dry-matter average, with a maximum of 7·5 tons/acre at 400–450 lb N/acre). Attempts to increase production of grass/clover swards by using N for early growth and relying on clover for mid-season growth were unsuccessful in 2 out of 3 years. As at Jealott's Hill, an all-grass sward required about 146 lb N/acre to give the same yield as an unfertilized grass/clover sward, but at Henley Manor the total yield was much greater and significantly more nitrogen was transferred from the clover to the accompanying grass. Experiments to establish the amount of nitrogen released by grass and grass/clover or predominantly-clover swards, to following wheat crops, showed that a one-year all-clover ley contributed some 110 lb/acre of nitrogen to the following crop, whilst the clover in a grass/clover ley contributed 60 lb of nitrogen. The unfertilized wheat crop following unfertilized cut grass yielded, on average, 1·2 tons grain per acre compared with 1·8 tons of grain from similar plots receiving 100 lb N/acre.

Arable Crops

Despite the dominance of the 'grassland' theme, a consequence of the impressive response shown by grass to nitrogen fertilizers, the early Jealott's Hill workers were alive to the need to study the effects of NPK fertilizers on cereals and other arable crops. The development of compound fertilizers from the late 1920s onwards called for extensive field trials of sowing rates, seed spacing, rates and timing of applications, trials which have provided the scientific basis of recommendations for the present range of ICI compound fertilizers. Conflict of opinion over the timing of nitrogen applications is not yet resolved, and may never be, because the 'correct' recommendation depends upon local soils and climates.

By contrast, other experiments (still continuing) include an examination of the nitrogen response of new varieties of both winter wheat and spring barley. There are indications that modern cereal varieties may have a somewhat higher response to nitrogen than have older varieties. In recent years there have been several occasions when the highest yields of winter wheat have been between 3·8 and 4·4 tons/ac (9·5 to 11·0 tonnes/ha) following the application of 168 lb/ac (188 kg/ha) nitrogen.

Present-day studies include precision seeding in relation to seed rates, and the possibility of increasing yields of winter wheat by using high levels of nitrogen in combination with fungicidal treatments.

Forms of Nitrogen Fertilizer

'Straights' and Mixtures

The three major plant nutrients, nitrogen, phosphorus and potassium were originally applied in 'straight' form, often as sulphate of ammonia, superphosphate and muriate of potash or in simple mixtures of two or more of these fertilizers. In the early 1920s, sulphate of ammonia (containing 20·5%N) was the only available source of synthetic nitrogen, but, within a few years, ammonium phosphates were used to replace much of the sulphate of ammonia and superphosphate used in mixtures, and a granular concentrated complete fertilizer (CCF) was produced by ICI. Experiments to determine optimum rates of NPK fertilizers for a wide range of crops began at Jealott's Hill in 1929 and, in 1930, trials began with a new product, 'Nitro-Chalk', which was a mixture of ammonium nitrate and chalk. It was extremely effective and quickly became the most commonly preferred nitrogenous fertilizer. An enthusiastic demonstration, possibly not in keeping with present-day aesthetic standards, displayed the name 'NITRO-CHALK' in letters consisting of increased grass growth on a Cleveland hillside. At first 'Nitro-Chalk' contained only 10% N but it was gradually improved, with support from Jealott's Hill trials, to an eventual 25% N product.

In the period 1928 to 1934 ICI carried out a series of field experiments on an extensive range of crops using urea as a straight nitrogen fertilizer; the general conclusion then was that, at the rates of application used (which were low by modern standards), urea behaved very similarly to ammonium sulphate and 'Nitro-Chalk'. However, trials in 1951–1961, with 'Urea-Chalk' (a mixture of urea and chalk containing 31% N) and, later, with urea as a straight nitrogen fertilizer, showed that, at high rates of application, urea was generally less effective than conventional forms of nitrogen, especially when top-dressed on grassland. Urea incorporated in NPK compounds also tended to be more harmful to germinating seedlings when combine-drilled, especially on calcareous soils. Pot-culture and laboratory experiments by A J Low and T E Tomlinson confirmed that the loss of efficiency and the damage to seedlings was accentuated under cold, dry conditions and the cause was attributed to hydrolysis of urea by the enzyme urease, with the formation of ammonium carbonate and the liberation of free ammonia [6].

Because of its very high nitrogen concentration (46%) and obvious advantages in reduced transport and handling costs, however, interest in urea remained strong, and other methods of rendering it more efficient were tried. These included trials by A E M Hood, H R Jameson and R Cotterell with the fertilizer combine-drilled in closely-spaced ($3\frac{1}{2}$–$4\frac{1}{2}$ inch) rows of cereals to reduce the rate of application per unit length of drill, placement to avoid contact with germinating seedlings, modification of the star-wheel mechanism of the combine-drill to reduce the characteristic cyclic distribution and hence damage by urea, and work (by T E Tomlinson and J R Anderson) on urease inhibition. Various chemicals displayed this latter property in screening tests, but whilst they showed promise in pot culture, they were unsuccessful in field experiments and, to this day, no effective and practical urease inhibitor has yet been discovered.

Experience gained at Jealott's Hill and elsewhere led to the conclusion that ICI's range of compound fertilizers had to be based on ammonium nitrate. In the early 1960s new compound-fertilizer plants were built, but additional straight-nitrogen fertilizer capacity was also required. Once again it was necessary to decide whether a new straight-nitrogen fertilizer should be urea based or ammonium nitrate based, and whether it should be liquid or solid. Many of the practical disadvantages of urea in compounds also applied to its use as a straight fertilizer. After much agronomic and process development work, ICI produced a concentrated ammonium nitrate fertilizer containing 34·5% N. The new product, 'Nitram', was a non-caking, free-flowing product containing an internal desiccant, and the first plant, capable of producing 350,000 tons/annum, was commissioned at Severnside in December 1964. Because of its superb handling properties and the fact that 3 bags of 'Nitram' were equivalent to 5 bags of 'Nitro-Chalk', 'Nitram' rapidly established itself as a market leader and gradually replaced 'Nitro-Chalk'. A second 'Nitram' plant followed in 1969, increasing the ICI capacity to 700,000 tons/annum, and a recent decision to build 'Nitram III' at Billingham will bring the total capacity to 1·2 million tons/annum from 1979 onwards.

Liquid Nitrogenous Fertilizers
After World War II the use of liquid nitrogenous fertilizers, and particularly anhydrous ammonia, became very popular in North America, where it enjoyed a price advantage for wide-row crops such as corn and cotton. Jealott's Hill field experimenters encountered many problems in investigating such techniques in the UK and had to develop small-plot equipment appropriate to UK conditions. In the 1950s and 1960s, thorough investigation showed that, although agronomic results on arable crops were satisfactory, neither anhydrous nor aqueous ammonia was as efficient as solid ammonium nitrate for use on grass, where the injection equipment available at the time tended to do lasting damage to the sward. Apart from agronomic considerations the application of liquid nitrogenous fertilizers to close-row crops in Britain carried high application costs and the storage and distribution equipment was expensive in capital for an individual farmer. The use of liquids is now developing on the basis of contract treatment by centrally organised distributors and thus may become more generally acceptable.

Slow-Release Fertilizers
In the 1800s Lawes and Gilbert at Rothamsted were in bitter conflict with von Liebig in Germany over the question of what manufactured plant nutrients were necessary for continued good cropping; ever since those days there has been a vociferous school of thought which holds that no good can come of any 'unnatural' farming practice and that the only acceptable plant foods are those derived from 'organic' sources. But quite apart from the superstitious distrust of the manufactured product, there is a more rational belief that the slower release of nutrients from 'organic' materials more closely matches the demands of the growing plant and must therefore be more efficient. In 1935 Lewis and Page undertook a series of experiments at Jealott's Hill in which they compared the nitrogen manuring value of several organic manures (shoddy, meat and bone-meal, hoof-meal, fish-meal, guano and dried blood) with that of sulphate of ammonia, using Brussels sprouts *(Brassica oleracea* var. *gemmifera)* as the test species. Their results showed that sulphate of ammonia produced by far the highest yields of sprouts in the field and a higher recovery of the applied nitrogen in the pot plants. In discussing the work Lewis commented that the slow nitrogen release rate of organic fertilizers was often a disadvantage and was recognised as such by growers who applied extra top dressings of soluble nitrogenous fertilizer to crops at critical times.

However, there is no denying the convenience of a slow-release fertilizer for many applications (e.g. amenity grass, and as a base fertilizer in glasshouse beds) and workers at Jealott's Hill persisted in their investigations. Natural organic manures are far too variable in performance to serve as standards for scientific investigation but a manufactured product might be expected to provide a high degree of uniformity in release rate. In 1936 Lewis investigated guanidine salts and found them to be inferior in overall fertilizer value to ammonium sulphate although, unlike other workers, he found no phytotoxic effects. In the mid-1960s two hydrolysis products of urea (ammeline and ammelide), urea-formaldehyde, and oxamide were all examined. Although pot-culture tests gave promising results, field experiments on spring barley were disappointing, the release of nitrogen being so slow, particularly with ammelide, that it was questionable whether the latter released any nitrogen at all. Oxamide (31·8% N) was the most promising on agronomic considerations, but its manufacturing cost was too high to be commercially viable.

Another product, isobutylidene diurea (IBDU) made by the Mitsubishi Corporation, gave promising results in pot tests, providing some release of nitrogen over a period of 12 weeks. In 1966, a series of field experiments compared the effect of IBDU with that of 'Nitram' on winter wheat; it was estimated that only 66% of the nitrogen in IBDU became available to the crop, and ammonium nitrate produced bigger yields. After further trials it was concluded that this material would be unsuitable for use as a general agricultural fertilizer, although its possible use on speciality crops was not excluded.

Finally, in 1968, Jealott's Hill examined a sulphur-coated urea made by the Tennessee Valley Authority; the material released its nitrogen over a 12-week period and pot-culture tests with grass showed a high recovery of the applied nitrogen, comparable with that obtained from repeated applications of ammonium nitrate. Trials with various experimental formulations showed that a 25% w/w sulphur coating gave a satisfactory compromise between adequate immediate action and slow release [7], and in 1972 this material, under the name 'Gold-N' was made available to UK growers.

In continuing trials on grass at Jealott's Hill between 1971 and 1974 the response to 'Gold-N' sometimes matched (wet summers) but sometimes fell short of (dry summers) that with 'Nitram' and, because of its apparent weather-dependence and higher costs, 'Gold-N' has not been recommended for grass production in commercial agriculture. While early supplies were made at Billingham, a medium-scale plant has since been built in Canada and this is designed to supply sulphur-coated urea to the amenity and horticultural markets both in North America and in Europe.

Grassland Management and Utilization

Commercially, grass is grown to feed cattle and sheep, and the increased grass production obtained from the use of nitrogen fertilizer can only be properly evaluated in terms of the meat and milk it produces. So the experimental use of fertilizers at Jealott's Hill went hand-in-hand with grassland management and feeding value studies.

Milk Production
The introduction of the electric fence made it possible to exploit grass by

rationing it within fields or paddocks on a daily or twice-daily basis rather than by normal paddock grazing. Trials at Jealott's Hill in 1949 and 1950 were inconclusive because of the practice, common in grazing trials of the day, of allocating different numbers of cows to the two systems; but the experience thus gained led to various systems of paddock grazing currently in common use. Between 1954 and 1957 grazing trials with spring-calving cows evaluated the effect of supplementary concentrate supplied to dairy cows at grass. The response was small and decidedly uneconomic but the trial demonstrated that dairy cows could produce up to 6 gallons (27 litres) of milk per head per day from grass alone during the spring flush without losing weight or condition.

During the 1960s, growing public concern with environmental matters gave rise to debate on the wisdom of various farming practices, of which the intensive management of grassland was one example. In particular, fears for the possible effect of increased nitrate in the herbage upon the health of ruminant animals, and the effect of leached fertilizers in field effluents upon the quality of drinking-water, were voiced. Ten years earlier, Low and Armitage had studied the drainage losses of nitrogen from clover, meadow fescue grass and fallow. Grass- and clover-covered lysimeters were cut at the grazing stage and the herbage dried, ground and returned to the soil surface, while the nitrogen and other nutrient contents of the drainage water were determined at intervals. Over the first three years of the trial the fallow lysimeter lost, on average, 108 lb N/acre/annum, the clover loss was 27 lb N/acre and the loss from the grass-cropped lysimeter was only 2–4 lb N/acre, which was less than the amount occurring in annual rainfall. By 1970 ICI had decided to support a much more comprehensive field-scale study, to determine what effects very high rates of nitrogenous fertilizer might have on (a) dairy cow performance, milk quality, fertility, longevity, health and blood constituents, and (b) the quality of the drainage water issuing from the field drains. Two rates of nitrogen fertilizer were chosen, 250 and 750 kg N/ha/annum, representing respectively twice and six times the average usage on dairy farms in England and Wales in 1975. The experiment proper began in April 1971 and the animal health studies were continued for five years. The drainage-water quality studies have now been carried on for six years and are still continuing. Records are kept of sward changes, the herbage is measured for yield and is chemically analysed; detailed soil studies are also carried out.

Results have shown conclusively that the higher rate of nitrogen fertilizer used in this trial, which is about twice that used by the most intensive dairy farmer, has not been detrimental to the performance or the health of Friesian dairy cows at any time throughout the trial. Nitrate levels in the grass were consistently high and blood serum urea concentrations were increased well above normal, but no animal suffered from this in any way. The cows continued to perform and thrive as well as those managed at the lower level of nitrogen fertilizer application. At the higher nitrogen level, the grass made into silage for winter feeding received 300 kg N/ha/cut, which is twice the rate normally recommended; the cows found this palatable, milked well and suffered no ill effects.

Drainage water issuing from the two areas receiving 250 and 750 kg N/ha was monitored on a continuous basis, sampled in proportion to the flow and analysed weekly for nutrients. At the lower rate of nitrogen, which is twice the national average on grassland in England and Wales, the average annual concentration of NO_3–N was always well below the WHO acceptable level of 22·6 mg/l. At the unrealistic level of 750 kg N/ha this concentration of NO_3–N was exceeded frequently but although only 40% (as opposed to 70% at the 250 kg N/ha level) of the fertilizer nitrogen was utilized by the grass, by no means all of the unused nitrogen was lost by leaching. The balance was possibly either immobilized in the soil organic matter or lost by denitrification [8].

The trial has shown quite convincingly that no constraints to the use of nitrogen fertilizer need apply, as far as the health of ruminants is concerned, up to rates of application well in excess of levels ever likely to be used in practice.

The debate on drainage-water quality continues, and work is in progress at Jealott's Hill to determine the fate of fertilizer nitrogen with greater precision. Little is known about the losses of nitrogen that occur as a result of denitrification in the sediment of ditches, streams, rivers, lakes and reservoirs, but an estimate can be made which shows that the levels of nitrate reaching the points of extraction for public supplies are only about half of the concentrations leaving the drainage outlets in the fields. It is believed that problems are only likely to occur, at practical levels of application, following prolonged periods of drought, when nitrate concentrations might exceed the WHO acceptable level.

Sheep
During the 1950s the effort devoted to intensifying grazing systems was gradually increased, with particular emphasis on beef and lamb production, and a great deal of work was done by ICI at Jealott's Hill and elsewhere to investigate intensive management systems for lowland sheep.

Many trials were conducted throughout the UK to find practical ways of intensifying sheep husbandry and, as part of a programme in conjunction with ICI's Pharmaceuticals Division, a series of related trials was carried out at Jealott's Hill to compare systems of management, to determine optimum nitrogen rates and associated stocking rates, to monitor disease problems, (in particular the build-up of internal parasites), and to evaluate remedial measures. These showed clearly that, over a wide range of stocking rates of ewes and lambs, set-stocking on one area was as productive as a rotational paddock system, and that under the former system the response to nitrogen in terms of grassland productivity could be converted to increased output of lamb and wool by keeping more stock per acre. The optimum nitrogen rate for this purpose at Jealott's Hill varied from year to year but results indicated that, when grass growth was not seriously limited by drought, 112–170 lb N/acre was justified, allowing 5–6 ewes plus twin lambs per acre to be supported, compared with only 4 ewes and twin lambs per acre where no fertilizer was applied but with clover in the sward. Collection and identification of parasitic worms showed that anthelmintic dosing was a very important requisite in an intensive system of sheep husbandry, particularly where the same field was used for more than one year and where ewes were introduced from elsewhere. Although this work was done some twenty years ago, the principles derived are still sound today and are practised by many graziers of low-land flocks.

Beef

In the early 1950s grazing-system studies on beef showed that, by the use of up to 335 lb N/acre, very satisfactory individual performance and output per acre could be obtained from the much higher stocking rates that were by then customary. Liveweight increase of the animals responded linearly to the fertilizer nitrogen rate up to 250 lb N/acre with a response of 1 lb liveweight-gain per 1 lb N. Supplementary feeding during the summer did not improve performance, and strip-grazing within paddocks appeared to be no more productive than paddocks alone.

In the three years from 1957 to 1959, comparison of a zero-grazing system with paddock grazing showed that the increased output of beef from zero-grazing was low, amounting only to an extra 5%. In 1966, however, a new 6-year series of trials began, using a completely different approach; the grass for zero-grazing was treated as a crop and was cut for feeding to stock at the early silage stage rather than at the normal grazing stage. By this means, extra digestible material could be produced and higher stocking rates could be supported. Although individual performance was slightly (4%) reduced, this was more than compensated for by an increase in stocking rate, and the gross margin per acre was 25% higher from this system of zero-grazing than from paddock grazing. This presented a viable and efficient system of beef production, but the year-round handling of slurry proved a major constraint to its wider introduction.

Unlike dairy cows, beef cattle could not be supported for a whole grazing season on a rigid two-sward system, the essence of which is an equal split into a grazing area and a silage area, because this does not supply sufficient grazing for growing animals after mid-season. Although set-stocking or continuous grazing throughout the season on a field basis was a traditional system for beef cattle on the renowned fattening pastures of the English Midlands, it had never been tried under intensive management using high rates of nitrogen fertilizer and high stocking rates. Consequently, in 1968, a two-field system was tested using the following régime: one field was set-stocked until mid-season; the other was cut for silage in May/June. Beef cattle were then dosed with anthelmintics and transferred to set-stock the silage aftermath. The previously grazed field was shut off for silage and, after this crop was taken, both fields became available for set-stock grazing in the autumn. So successful, and easy to use, was this novel system that within two years it had been developed into the ICI '1-2-3' or 'Two-Field' system for spring and autumn-born beef cattle and for dairy young stock [9].

In large-scale trials at the Leaths Farm in S W Scotland set-stocking was then applied to dairy cows, and compared with a 21-day paddock system. Its success led to the development of the ICI 'Full Graze' system.

Forage Conservation

Fifty years ago grass was generally considered to be not so much a crop as a natural, and distinctly seasonal, phenomenon over which the farmer had little or no control. The grassland studies in the early years of Jealott's Hill had set out to demonstrate that, by the use of fertilizers, grass could be the most valuable source of protein on the route to milk production, and from the outset the need for forage of high feeding value during the winter months was recognised. Pioneer work on the conservation of grass and other crops, much of which was carried out in collaboration with H E Woodman and his colleagues at the School of Agriculture, Cambridge, was an important feature of the early Jealott's Hill research programme.

The freedom, insisted on by Sir Frederick Keeble, to undertake fundamental research without the need to show immediate commercial benefits, encouraged S J Watson and W S Ferguson to embark on an ambitious and comprehensive programme of investigations into the processes of silage-making, hay-making and grass-drying, and the evaluation of these conserved forages as food for cattle.

The wealth of scientific experiments and practical trials carried out in these early years has been recorded by Watson himself in his published texts on crop conservation [10]. The suitability of various crops for conservation, and the effects of stage of growth on the composition and yield of nutrients were studied. The range of crops examined spanned pasture grasses, cereals, root crops, brassicas and even bracken.

Studies on conservation processes included hay-making and the artificial drying of crops, and an extensive series of investigations of ensilage. The experiments covered losses in conservation processes, the use of chemical additives, types of silo, and the utilization of conserved crops by ruminant animals. Studies of the chemical changes in the composition of silages were also conducted.

The most important studies on hay-making concerned the crude-protein content of hay crops. The surveys and trials carried out at Jealott's Hill showed that hay had, in general, a relatively low crude-protein content— usually less than 10% of the dry-matter. Cutting the crop at an earlier stage of growth gave a higher yield per acre of protein equivalent than was obtained from more mature crops. Some American work was also followed up to demonstrate that the application of a late top-dressing of nitrogen fertilizer gave an increase in both the crude-protein content and the digestibility of hay.

The work on ensilage showed that it was important to restrict the amount of air trapped in the silage mass, thus promoting a cold fermentation process, which gave reduced nutrient losses and high nutritional value. It also demonstrated that it was essential to promote a rapid increase in acidity to produce a good quality silage. The direct addition of inorganic acids (as in the A.I. Virtanen process) or the addition of molasses (to provide extra sugars to promote microbial production of acids) were considered to be the best techniques for obtaining this rapid acidification, and resulted in better quality silage.

This early work also concluded that the best type of silo was the tower silo, but that good quality silage could nevertheless be made in a pit or a trench. The making of silage rather than hay was encouraged, because work at Jealott's Hill had shown that lower nutrient losses and higher nutritional values were obtained with silage than with hay.

The discovery that young, fresh grass with a high protein content could be artificially dried, led to hopes of producing a home-grown fodder with a nutritional value high enough to be a substitute for expensive, imported high protein feeds. The Jealott's Hill studies were concerned with such aspects as the effects of drying temperature on the chemical composition and digestibility of dried forage crops, and the nutritional evaluation of the products. Experiments with beef cattle and dairy cows showed that the nutritive value of dried grass was equal to that of most commercial 'cakes', provided that the quality of the grass used (especially the protein content) was high. At this time, additives were not used in butter to maintain or enhance the yellow colour; the carotene content of forages was therefore regarded as important for maintaining butter colour and dried grass was particularly useful in this respect. Engineering developments by ICI at Billingham resulted in the construction of the 'Billingham' drier; first marketed in 1936, this drier not only became the most popular make in the UK, but led to a succession of improved models.

Despite the impressive results that could be obtained by feeding dried grass, however, the technique of grass-drying never really caught on. One of the more obvious reasons for this failure was the high cost of fuel to run the driers, but the high capital outlay also deterred farmers from buying driers. Although, when processed by the Jealott's Hill technique, dried grass had a high nutritional value, the product was very variable in quality—in practice, it could only be as good as the grass that was grown—and it was too bulky when compared with cake.

The approach of World War II, and the recognition that home-produced feeding-stuffs were a vital element in the country's efforts to achieve self-sufficiency, turned Jealott's Hill's attention to processes for improving the feeding value of straw. In 1938 Slade, Watson and Ferguson revived a process developed towards the end of the last century by Kellner in Germany; straw was heated with caustic soda to produce a feed of improved digestibility, but the Jealott's Hill process used milder conditions and caused less degradation of the more valuable components. The treatment involved soaking the straw in 1·5% caustic soda solution for about 20 hours at ambient temperature and its final feeding value compared well with that of more traditional forages.

The war over, however, the few farmers who had been pulping straw were more than glad to revert to concentrate feeding; but it is interesting to note that, with the feeding of Man's own staple foodstuffs to animals coming increasingly under scrutiny, there is currently a re-awakening of interest in straw processing for animal feed.

Looking back on the early work on forage conservation at Jealott's Hill, it seems that, perhaps, the most notable contribution to agriculture was the pioneer work that did much to promote the acceptance of ensilage as a practical farm technique. Indeed, the knowledge built up at Jealott's Hill gained for ICI a high reputation in the field—sufficient in fact for the war-time Government to send agricultural advisers on training courses at Jealott's Hill to help initiate the National Silage Campaign of the 1940s.

Despite the efforts of Watson, Ferguson and colleagues, however, it is only in the last ten years or so that there has been a really major increase in the proportion of grass conserved as silage in the UK. Did Watson and his colleagues fail to communicate their ideas and results to farmers? Or was it another case of a grateful return, after war-time shortages, to cheap, plentiful and convenient, though largely imported, concentrated feeding-stuffs? What is certain is that, even at Jealott's Hill, forage conservation received little attention for the next twenty years.

When, in 1967, interest was again directed to this topic, it was in a very different atmosphere from that prevailing in the pre-war years. Agricultural Division's fertilizer mainstay had become a hard, competitive business, and emphasis now was very much on the development of products that would not only provide benefits to agriculture, but would also be of direct commercial advantage to ICI.

The target of this new approach to forage conservation work was the development of grass silage additives—products that could both control and restrict the silage fermentation processes. The work called for sequential testing programmes involving microbiological, chemical and ruminant nutrition studies. The first stages involved the selection of potentially useful chemicals from *in vitro* laboratory tests against cultures of the bacteria and fungi that they were required to control. The best compounds were then tested on grass for silage to provide material for a chemical evaluation of their effectiveness in fermentation control. Larger-scale trials using farm machinery to prepare sufficiently large quantities of silage for animal feeding trials then followed, while studies on the toxicology and safety of use of candidate products also formed an important part of the work. As a result of a successful development programme by N Watchorn, I H Pike and F Bellingham the grass silage additive 'Sylade' was launched on the UK market in 1972, where its efficacy rapidly became appreciated.

The product, a formalin/sulphuric acid mixture, when applied to grass for silage at 5 litres/tonne, restricts fermentation, thus preventing undesirable clostridial development that results in butyric acid production and protein breakdown. 'Sylade' gives a silage with a lower acid content that is much more palatable to livestock. Additional advantages of formalin-containing silage additives include a measure of protection of forage proteins from breakdown in the rumen because of binding of the formalin in the additive with the proteins. This has the desirable result that more undegraded protein gets through to the small intestine of the ruminant animal, where it is readily absorbed and metabolised. Extensive independent trials with 'Sylade' have shown that, on average, the intake of treated silage by beef animals is about 10% higher than that for untreated silage, with resulting liveweight gains of more than 0·2 kg/head/day greater for animals receiving the 'Sylade'-treated silage. Other studies have shown significant improve-

2

Fertilizer distribution old style

1 Fertilizing grassland
2 Hand distribution
3 Filling the drill

1

Silage making old style

1 Pit silo, Jealott's Hill
2 Wooden tower silo

2

2

3

4

Fertilizer use, old and new

1 'Nitro-chalk' advertisement 1951
2 Man-handling 'Nitro-Chalk'
   1930s
3 Bulk handling 'Nitram'
4 Filling distributor with 'Nitram'

Harvesting grass, present-day.

Photo: Tony Evans

ments in milk yields of dairy cows fed silage made with formalin/acid additives.

More recently, exploratory research has included studies on preservatives for moist grain and moist hay, and on more advanced grass preservatives. Work on ruminant nutrition has focused mainly on the use of urea and its derivatives as non-protein nitrogen sources for ruminant animals. Experiments with urea itself helped to establish safe levels of incorporation of urea in feed supplements, and gave ICI a valuable practical understanding of the use of urea in feeds. There have also been exploratory studies with slow-release forms of non-protein nitrogen such as urea phosphate and isobutylidene diurea, but no commercially significant justification for the use of such materials has been found.

Agricultural Development

The boundary between research and development is nowhere more indefinite than in agricultural science. ICI has long recognised this problem and, at an early stage, promoted parallel work on the development farms to test, exploit and demonstrate the results of Jealott's Hill research. For example, grass is grown mostly for animal feed, and conclusions drawn from trials on small plots, which are perfectly adequate for cereals and root crops, are often misleading where grassland utilization is concerned. In agricultural practice, the development of effective systems of grazing management and the measurement of success in financial as well as in physical terms are important issues. Such issues have been examined on the ICI farms, and a useful technique to emerge from this programme was the farmlet approach first operated at Henley Manor during the five years 1957–62. The technique comprised the setting aside of a specific area of land with a single dominant farming objective, with its own buildings and specialised labour and machinery. The first carefully monitored investigation of this kind showed a clear relationship between fertilizer nitrogen, stocking rate and profitability, and had a significant effect upon agriculturists' views, both within ICI and elsewhere, on the respective roles of fertilizer nitrogen and clover in intensive grass production. A new system of farm accounting was developed at this time which allowed the financial performances of such farmlets to be expressed in terms of gross margin per acre. The technique also allowed the farm to pursue a variety of livestock projects in a form that was particularly effective for demonstration to visitors.

As a result of the Henley Manor success with the farmlet system, other ICI development farms gradually adopted this approach. An important outcome of such work at The Leaths, in Scotland, was the development of a successful dairy by-product beef system using the Ayrshire cow and Beef Shorthorn top-crossing bulls. The 'Full Graze' system, already described and now widely practised, was also a product of such trials at the Leaths.

The Jealott's Hill dairy herd has been used primarily for the high-nitrogen trial, and the dairy by-product beef enterprise has been the focal point for a wide range of experimental work with grazing systems, both described earlier. Wilton, which is also run as several farmlets, has been primarily concerned with the development of single-suckler beef systems to suit lowland as well as upland conditions, and Henley Manor itself now operates as several farmlets assessing the problems and profitability of autumn and spring-calving dairy cows and intensive self-contained heifer rearing at 2-year calving.

At Dairy House in Cheshire, special emphasis throughout the years has been given to the development of high-quality silage-making techniques and to the practical assessment, initially of mechanical, and later of chemical, aids to ensilage—such as 'Sylade'. The main dairy herd, established in 1968, has concentrated on a large-scale evaluation of zero-grazing.

Investigations within ICI's control, whether research at Jealott's Hill or studies at one of the development farms can form only a small part of the input to agricultural progress. Records from practical farmers are essential to the long-term evaluation of novel techniques and ICI has, since 1945, become progressively more deeply involved with the collection of such records from a wide range of different types of farming. Under its Chief Development Officer, A S Barker, and his team of agricultural development officers, CAC initiated (a) a Farm Management Investigation of 20 fully recorded farms and, (b) a Grassland Management Investigation with, initially, 80 mainly grassland dairy farms from which only records of their grass-based enterprises were obtained. Experience gained in the first year of ICI's Grassland Management Investigation showed, however, that a partially-costed scheme that only obtained details of grassland enterprises would not allow a proper evaluation of grassland management practices as they affected the occupier of a mixed farm and, since 1948, the ICI Costed Farm Scheme has included only records from whole farm businesses.

Information gathered in the early years of the Grassland Management Investigation was used for case studies of successful farm businesses and for a more detailed examination of the role of grass in the economics of milk production, as well as for studies of specific aspects of grassland husbandry, e.g. ley establishment. As the scheme progressed, the accumulation of detailed records from a large group of farmers, all striving for increased profitability through better grassland management, provided the opportunity for a unique statistical study, by J Clark and J E Bessell [11], of the relevant input/output relationships, which established a strong correlation between increasing use of nitrogen fertilizer and increased milk production and profit per acre.

With the arrival of a large and powerful computer at Billingham the ability to handle and analyse farm management data was expanded to around 250 farms in England and Wales alone and the opportunity was taken to examine the application of linear programming methods as an aid to better farm planning. As a result the 'MASCOT' system of computerised linear programming was developed by ICI until it is now probably the most advanced in the UK. It has been devised especially to assist managers of large and complex farming businesses in the choice of the optimum combination and size of enterprises to give the best results from all the resources at their command. Since it was first offered commercially in autumn 1969 close on 600 farmers have made use of 'MASCOT'. Experience gained in the development of the 'MASCOT' programme and the preparation of farm management statements from the ICI Monthly Recorded Farm Scheme, led naturally to the development of a system of financial planning, launched under the name of ICI 'CASHPLAN' in February 1971. This system uses the basic farm plan to produce a gross margin budget and, by incorporating interest payments, re-investment, taxation and personal drawings it produces an overall cashflow for the following year. Over 700 farmers in the British Isles have used this unique service since its introduction six years ago. But unmistakably the most popular scheme has been ICI 'DAIRYMAID' which is currently used by 3000 of the leading milk producers in England and Wales as well as by 2000 of their counterparts in other European countries for a monthly comparison of their herd performance.

The variety of agricultural problems that merited attention 50 years ago was formidable and it was clearly necessary for Jealott's Hill to be selective in its choice of research topics. From those chosen, much valuable information and several novel techniques have emerged and their application has undoubtedly contributed to the success of commercial farming in Britain. It should not be forgotten how great is that success; in the 50 years between 1927 and 1977 agricultural production in terms of yield per hectare from the major crops and milk-yield per cow has virtually doubled. Wheat yields in England and Wales increased from 2·12 to 4·90 tonnes/ha, barley yields from 1·85 to 4·40 tonnes/ha. In the same period labour productivity has greatly increased, with the farm tractor early replacing the horse as the source of power for all field work. Fertilizer use has increased dramatically; nitrogen consumption alone has risen from 40,500 tonnes of 'synthetic' nitrogen in 1926/7 until it is now at the million tonne mark and its further expansion to 1·5 million tonnes within the next ten years has been forecast.

It is in the nature of science that the solution to one problem often gives the investigator insight to pose others of greater precision. The last fifty years of agricultural progress provide no reason to suppose that this will not continue to be so; advances in cognate sciences, such as plant breeding, open more doors than they close and opportunities for agricultural achievement within the next fifty years are at least as prolific as they were fifty years ago.

References

[1] Greenhill A W (1930) 'Investigations into the intensive system of grassland management, (1) The chemical composition of intensively treated pasture' *J. Agric. Sci.* **20**, 573–86

[2] Jones M G (1933) 'Grassland management and its influence on the sward, (1) Factors influencing the growth of pasture plants' *Emp. J. exp. Agric.* **1**, 43–7

[3] Blackman G E (1938) 'The interaction of light intensity and nitrogen supply on the growth and metabolism of grasses and clover *(Trifolium repens)*, (1) The effect of light intensity and nitrogen supply on the clover content of a sward' *Ann. Bot.*, London, **2**, 257–80

[4] Hood A E M, Procter J (1961) 'An intensive cereal growing experiment' *J. agric. Sci.* **57**, 241–7

[5] Low A J (1972) 'The effect of cultivation on the structure and other physical characteristics of grassland and arable soils (1945–1970)' *J. Soil Sci.* **23,** 363–80

[6] Tomlinson T E (1970) 'Urea agronomic applications' The Fertilizer Soc. Proc. 113

[7] Davies L H (1976) 'Slow-release fertilizers particularly sulphur-coated urea' The Fertilizer Soc. Proc. 153

[8] Hood A E M (1976) 'The high-nitrogen trial on grassland at Jealott's Hill' *Stikstof* **83/84,** 395–404

[9] Hood A E M, Bailie J H (1973) 'A new grazing system for beef cattle—the 2 field system' *J. Br. Grassld Soc.* **28,** 101–8

[10] Watson S J (1939) *The Science and practice of conservation. Grass and forage crops.* Fertilizer & Feeding Stuffs Journal, London. 2 vols. 820 pp.

[11] Clark J, Bessell J E (1956) *Profits from dairy farming,* Imperial Chemical Industries Limited, Central Agricultural Control. Bull. No. 7

Jealott's Hill buildings 1956

Chapter 3

Seed treatments

Although Jealott's Hill had been conceived as part of a programme to spread the gospel of more profit from farming by the use of nitrogenous fertilizers, the new parent company, ICI, inherited, via the British Dyestuffs Corporation, an early interest in crop protection, in the shape of fungicidal seed treatments.

Mercurial Fungicides

I G Farben's 1927 patent for the use of organo-mercurials as seed dressings led, in 1932, to the commissioning, by the then Dyestuffs Group, of a plant to produce 'Agrosan' G, a powder formulation containing 1·5% organically combined mercury as tolyl mercury acetate (TMA). 'Agrosan' G had its defects; it was inferior to some competitive products in its control of oat smut *(Ustilago avenae)* and bunt of wheat *(Tilletia caries)* and was particularly poor for the control of leaf stripe of oats *(Pyrenophora avenae)*. With the opening at Jealott's Hill, in 1936, of the Hawthorndale Laboratories, a small team led by G Watts Padwick (Imperial Mycologist, Government of India 1939–45 and, later, a Director of Plant Protection Ltd and Vice-President ICI (US)) began to seek means of improving the efficiency of the product.

An early consideration at Hawthorndale concerned the method of testing large numbers of fungicidal seed dressings. German plant pathologists had developed a technique for comparing chemicals, known from agar plate tests to have some fungicidal properties, by applying them, suitably diluted with inert dusts, to grain infested with spores of smut fungi; the seed was then germinated and an examination made both of the spores on the grain surface for germination, and of the grain and meristematic tissue for infection. This certainly worked but it was tedious and time-consuming; it was a relatively short and practical step to grow plants in soil, thus simulating natural conditions; but the cautious arrival at this solution reflects the pure science parentage of plant pathology at this time. Tests for controlling leaf stripe of oats could be done very successfully in small containers, and it was found quite practical to use a thousand boxes or more, involving as many as fifty chemicals, in one test. The work could be done in a few weeks.

For the cereal smuts, plants had to be grown to maturity, and the 'rod-row' plots used by plant breeders in the field were adopted; the row length was reduced to accommodate only 100 or 200 seeds per replicate, but the name 'rod-row' stuck. Here, truly natural conditions obtained, but the labour required at sowing time was a problem. There was an occasion in the autumn of 1936 when more than 2000 such 'rod-rows' had to be sown in one experiment with wheat for the control of bunt. Most of the staff at Hawthorndale joined in this effort, but, because of the size of the experiment half the replicates had to be sown one day and the remainder the next. When results were recorded months later it was found that the level of infection in the three replicates sown on the first day was some seven times as high as it was in those planted the next day; but the general order of efficacy of the various treatments was quite comparable. Such experiments showed that part of the TMA could be replaced, with advantage, by ethyl mercury chloride (EMC), a volatile alkyl mercury compound; control of leaf stripe resulted, together with a general improvement in control of the other cereal diseases. But the mystery of the seven-fold difference in infection between one day's sowing and the next was never solved.

With the advent of World War II, mercury, normally imported from Spain and Yugoslavia, became, like many other raw materials, difficult to obtain. By 1942 it was crucial to determine whether the level of mercury could be reduced without losing the property of adequate disease control. Trials conducted by R V Tipler between 1942 and 1944 showed that a mixture of phenyl mercury acetate (PMA I, page 34) and EMC could replace the TMA/EMC mixture without loss of activity, whilst the concentration of mercury could be reduced from 1·5 to 1·0%. A petroleum-soluble dye added to the formulation enabled the distribution of dressing on the seed to be checked. The new product, 'Agrosan' GN, was launched in 1945 and remained the standard powder seed dressing on the ICI range for 30 years.

Because the bulk of seed is machine-dressed by experienced operators, 'Agrosan' GN was accepted as a tolerably 'safe' product; but mercury compounds, and particularly the volatile alkyl mercury salts such as EMC, are inherently toxic. And powder seed treatments, particularly dusty formulations, are, without doubt, a potential hazard to workers in the seed treatment plant and to farmers drilling the seed. Not only concern for safety in handling, but problems in obtaining good adhesion and retention of powder on the seed, led, in the 1950s, to interest in liquid mercurial seed treatments, based on such compounds as methyl mercury dicyandiamide (MMD) and methyl mercury nitrile (MMN) [1]. These liquid dressings overcame the dust problem and had good adhesion to the seed, but redistribution from seed to seed was poor, and careful formulation was required as many of the solvents used in formulation were liable to affect germination and subsequent growth.

A process for the manufacture of MMD was developed at Jealott's Hill by E Sherlock and others, and manufacture, in the hands of J M Winchester and N W Drewe, started at Yalding in 1959. Two products were made: 'Agrosol' (mercurial only) and 'Ceresol' (mercury/heptachlor): but, even as liquids, the use of volatile alkyl mercury compounds such as MMD was not particularly desirable and eventually, in 1974, both products were withdrawn.

Non-mercurial Fungicides

It would be wrong to suppose that a sense of responsibility in the use of chemicals as crop protection aids has arisen only in recent years. But, 'needs must when the Devil drives'. The introduction of organomercurial compounds as fungicidal seed treatments in the 1930s gave the cereal grower, for the first time, insurance against crop failure. Mercury was effective, and still is, but it has always been recognised as a potentially dangerous material, and considerable effort has gone into the search for acceptable alternatives.

With the opening of the Hawthorndale Laboratories in 1936, tests commenced on a wide range of compounds as fungicidal seed treatments against cereal diseases. One which showed promise early was thiram (tetramethyl thiuram disulphide, **II,** page 34), first synthesised by du Pont chemists in 1931, which was found to be particularly active against *Pythium* spp. and *Fusarium* spp. A weakness of organo-mercurials is that they are ineffective against *Pythium,* a serious pathogen of vegetables, cotton and several other important crops such as maize and soya beans. Thiram was introduced by ICI in 1940 as a 10% powder for the control of soil-borne diseases of flax, under the name 'Nomersan' ('no mer' cury). The name was later changed to 'Fernasan' and its use extended to vegetable crops, peas and cotton. 'Nomersan' W, containing thiram and hexachlorbenzene (HCB), was introduced in 1943 as a non-mercurial treatment for cereals, but found little favour in competition with the more cost-effective organomercurials. It was to be another ten years before significant effort could be devoted to the search for a non-mercurial fungicidal seed-dressing; the rediscovery of the insecticidal properties of benzene hexachloride and its application in conjunction with organo-mercurials as a dual-purpose seed treatment, and the cotton black-arm seed-dressing programme (described in later chapters), left little time for speculative research on new chemicals.

By 1960, however, fungicidal activity had been discovered in a group of arylhydrazonoisoxazolones. The first examples, prepared by Dyestuffs Division chemists, were shown by H M Fox and R V Offield at Jealott's Hill to be active as seed treatments. Of a large number of analogues prepared drazoxolon (**III,** page 34) was considered to be the most suitable for development, though, because of its broad-spectrum fungicidal properties, most of the effort was directed towards foliar diseases, particularly those on apples, blackcurrants and cereals. As a seed treatment, however, it had good activity against *Pythium* and *Fusarium* and was about twice as effective as captan or thiram against these organisms on crops such as peas and beans.

Scottish Agricultural Industries Ltd, who sell grass seed, carried out trials which showed that drazoxolon controlled a range of soil-borne diseases of grass which are particularly prevalent in Scotland.

One problem with drazoxolon was that the compound was bright yellow and treating seed with a powder dressing resulted in yellow operators! This was obviated by formulating the chemical as an aqueous suspension of fine particles, or 'col'. The new formulation gave good cover and retention on the seed without phytotoxicity and overcame the dust problem in application; the product was launched in 1968 as 'SAIsan' for treatment of grass seed and as 'Mil-Col' for use on peas and beans.

The modifications to seed treatment machinery necessitated by the application of the relatively large quantities of the liquids 'Mil-Col' and 'SAIsan' proved invaluable in the development, some years later, of the cereal mildew fungicide 'Milstem'.

Seed Treatment Machinery

ICI's historical interest in the manufacture of seed treatment chemicals led naturally to an involvement with the machinery needed to apply these treatments efficiently on seed merchants' premises. In the mid-1950s there were numerous commercially available treaters on the UK market, of which the Robinson, the Strickland and the Turner were the best known. All were for the application of powder products, but interest in liquid treatments was growing (largely due to Swedish practice) and development work on a new machine had begun at Fernhurst.

Fernhurst has always been, and still is, the location for research into the mechanics of application of novel materials and techniques arising out of Jealott's Hill discoveries; and whilst it was not until 1964 that this was administratively rationalised by the transference of Machinery Department to R & D Jealott's Hill, it is impossible to chronicle the history of research at Jealott's Hill without acknowledging the absolutely essential contribution of a Department which might appear geographically not to be part of the Jealott's Hill story. But this input will crop up time and again in subsequent chapters, and it is as well to have explained here the basis for its inclusion in this narrative.

Development of the new seed treater, then, by D Maddison, R Watts and D A Harris took place at Fernhurst. The 'Plantector', as the new machine was called, was an improvement on all previous machines in that it was compact, had volumetric rather than weight sensing of seed feed, was fully automatic and required no adjustment between types of seed. It was soon modified by the addition of an accurate powder dispenser to make a multi-purpose machine. Seven prototypes were built and these worked very well in Britain for a number of years [2].

As with any new piece of equipment there were 'teething' troubles but constant modification had produced, by 1964, a reliable and, with the addition of protective 'cut-out' devices and guarding, a safe machine, four hundred of which were produced. In the UK, it has been the standard seed

2

3

Strip and paddock grazing

1 Grassland management
  experiment 1947
2 Strip grazing dairy herd 1965
3 Young beef cattle

1 Dressing seed with 'Agrosan' G
2 BHC bioassay (1949)
3 Locust cultures
4 Early wireworm trial on oats
  1947: left, seed with fungicide
  only; right, seed treated with
  'Mergamma'
5 'Rotostat' seed treater

treater for many years, gradually replacing the original powder machines. The 'Plantector' has been produced under licence in France for a number of years and small but regular exports are made to Africa. The concept of volumetric feed with auger mixing was developed in 1959 into the 'Plantector' Cotton Seed Treater for application of 'Perecot' 45 (cuprous oxide powder) which captured and retained for ICI markets for powder products in N Nigeria and Tanzania. Machines installed in Tanzania in 1960 are still working and operate, in the season, night and day with minimal supervision. Further machines have been installed at intervals and there are now twenty-four in operation there. A new market in Ghana has recently received its first machine.

As seed treatment chemicals changed, so the 'Plantector' was modified. Originally conceived as a liquid treater, but used mainly as a powder machine, the liquid circuit was later adapted to handle 'Milstem', which had presented considerable problems due to its sticky nature and large volume application; and the availability of the 'Plantector' in seed mills was an important factor in the rapid establishment of 'Milstem' in the UK market.

But the 'Plantector', whilst it was efficient at applying powders, was less satisfactory than had been hoped in the even application of liquids. This had not been a problem with the volatile mercury compounds such as MMD whose activity made up for inadequacy of distribution on the seed.

By the late 1960s however, it was realised that improvements were needed. Both the adhesion and retention of powders and the distribution of liquids on seed in commercial practice were recognised as less than satisfactory; seed merchants required a higher throughput than the six tons per hour of which the 'Plantector' was capable, and the machine had reached the limit of further modification.

This was the situation in 1970 when Machinery Development Group was approached by J F Milik, a consulting engineer who had invented a novel mixing device. Consisting of a saucer-shaped rotary member surrounded by a stationary cylinder, it had originally been conceived as a metal-finishing tool, in which machined objects were attached to the static walls and an abrasive slurry was washed over them by the rotating floor; but Milik recognised that it could be used for a variety of mixing applications. For seed treatment the floor was rotated and seeds put into the vessel were spun up the stationary walls. Slowed down by friction, they fell back into the rotor in the centre, and the result was a doughnut-shaped mass of seed engaged in a constant writhing motion. At Jealott's Hill, M R Middleton and R T Taylor showed that distribution of powders, liquids and cols was very even [3].

The idea was discussed enthusiastically, but one feature caused concern. The machine, ideally, treated seeds in batches—not continuously as was required by seed mills. This apparent snag became a distinct advantage with the realisation that, by standardising the batch size, the seed could be pre-weighed, treated, and discharged directly into bags, thus eliminating the holding hopper and the weighing of treated seeds which had long been troublesome. Also, the continuous scouring of the mixer walls by the seed made the machine self-cleaning. As the machine had a rotor and a stator it was given the name 'Rotostat'. The next three years saw it scaled up, given an automatic chemical dispenser and control system. By December 1976, twenty-two 'Rotostat' machines were treating an estimated quarter of the merchant-produced cereal seed in the UK, and this proportion will continue to increase. Even now, development is not complete, for teething problems still persist, but the 'Rotostat' is established and bids fair to revolutionize the large-scale commercial treatment of seed [4].

$$\text{HgOCOCH}_3 \qquad\qquad (\text{CH}_3)_2\text{N.}\overset{\text{S}}{\overset{\|}{\text{C}}}\text{.S.S.}\overset{\text{S}}{\overset{\|}{\text{C}}}\text{.N}\ (\text{CH}_3)_2$$

I phenylmercury acetate (PMA)   **II** thiram

III drazoxolon

Insecticidal and 'Dual-purpose' Treatments

The discovery, in 1942, of the remarkable activity against wireworm *(Agriotes* spp) and flea-beetle *(Phyllotreta* spp) of benzene hexachloride, and particularly of its gamma isomer, was quickly followed by field evaluation of gamma-BHC as seed treatments both alone and combined with mercurial fungicides, and the marketing from 1949 onwards of the 'Mergamma' range of dual-purpose seed dressings for cereals and sugar beet and 'Gammasan' against flea beetle on brassica crops. This work, however, more appropriately forms part of a later chapter, as does the development of organophosphorus insecticidal seed treatments.

References

[1] Callan I W M (1975) 'Achievements and limitations of seed treatments' *Outl. Agric.* **8** (5), 271–274
[2] Harris D A (1975) 'The application of chemicals to seed' *Outl. Agric.* **8** (5), 275–280
[3] Middleton M R (1973) 'Assessment of performance of the "Rotostat" seed treater' *Proc 7th Br. Insectic. Fungic. Conf.* p. 357–363
[4] Elsworth J E, Harris D A (1973) 'The "Rotostat" Seed Treater—a new application system' *Proc. 7th Br. Insectic. Fungic. Conf.* p. 349–355

Chapter 4

Selective herbicides

Weed control has been practised in a variety of crops since mediaeval times, without recourse to the use of chemicals. Provided the crop rows were wide enough apart weeds between the rows could be removed by hand or mechanical hoes, which limited their numbers to those weeds growing in the row.

With cereals, formerly sown broadcast and then in narrow drill widths, the problem was much more complex; although materials like copper sulphate and sulphuric acid had been used for many years for the selective control of weeds in cereals, they were only effective in a limited way and, as late as the 1930s, it was not uncommon to see farm labourers working their way through corn fields removing weeds by hand or with small 'spudding' tools.

This situation was about to change radically, as a result of a growing awareness among plant physiologists of the presence in plants of what were first called 'auxins' and, later, phytohormones—naturally occurring chemicals which regulate the processes of growth in plants as, by a simplistic analogy, do the endocrine hormones in animals.

F W Went, working in Holland, isolated the first such substance in 1926 and summarised the results of his experiments with the material in the terse statement: 'no growth without growth substance'. A few years later (1934) F Kögl and his associates in Holland isolated from urine a compound with the same plant-growth regulating properties as Went's 'auxin'. This proved to be a known compound, β-indoleacetic acid (IAA); its presence in plant tissues was confirmed, and it was found to be highly active in promoting growth and root formation from cuttings, and to be one of the chemicals essential in the determination of plant form and function.

The following year, workers at the Boyce Thompson Institute in New York reported that the related chemicals α-naphthylacetic acid (NAA) and β-indolebutyric acid, among others, were active in promoting plant growth and it was recognised that these synthetic substances could have important commercial applications, such as the rooting of cuttings and the control of pre-harvest drop in fruit trees.

In 1936, workers at Jealott's Hill were studying the role of organic matter in soil on plant growth. They foresaw the possibility that the organic fraction might contain growth hormones from decayed plants and that the soil might in this way stimulate plant growth. Preliminary trials using IAA and NAA were laid down at several nurseries using cuttings of a variety of crops and, later, trials were carried out at the Royal Botanic Gardens at Kew. Many species responded to the chemicals with increases in the bulk and number of roots produced.

In pursuit of the growth-stimulation theory, IAA and NAA were incorporated in soil in which cuttings and whole plants were grown. Then followed a revolutionary observation: NAA not only failed to stimulate plant growth but depressed it, and the depression was observed to be selective; the now classic experiments carried out in 1940 by W G Templeman showed that 25 lb/ac NAA killed yellow charlock *(Brassica sinapis)* without harming oats when the two were sown together, and irrespective of whether the application was made before or after emergence of the seedlings. By present-day standards this was an enormous dose of chemical but, even so, although the charlock was killed, the oats remained unharmed.

Subsequent tests with a range of compounds prepared or selected by W A Sexton at Dyestuffs Division, in Manchester, showed that many substituted naphthoxyacetic and phenoxyacetic acids could also inhibit plant growth, and that greater plantain *(Plantago major)* and yarrow *(Achillea millefolium)* reacted like yellow charlock; other cereals (rye, barley and wheat) were resistant to these chemicals as oats had been to NAA.

MCPA and 2,4-D

By November 1941 it was clear that the sodium salt of 4-chloro-2-methylphenoxyacetic acid, later known as MCPA or 'Methoxone', was one of the most active of the compounds tested, and that it depressed the germination and early seedling growth of corn buttercup *(Ranunculus arvensis)*, fat hen *(Chenopodium album)*, corn marigold *(Chrysanthemum segetum)*, corn spurrey *(Spergula arvensis)*, and field poppy *(Papaver rhoeas)* at concentrations which were without effect on cereals. Pot and field experiments showed that germination of yellow charlock was suppressed and plants at any stage from seedling to flowering were killed by spraying with solutions of MCPA at rates equivalent to approximately 1 lb acid per acre. Other compounds which showed marked activity included 2,4-dichlorophenoxyacetic acid, later known as 2,4-D, and the sodium salt and esters of β-naphthoxyacetic acid. R E Slade, then Research Controller of ICI, reported these findings to the Agricultural Research Council, to be told that similar discoveries had been made during 1942 at Rothamsted leading to work with 2,4-D, which had already found some use in the USA as a growth modifier.

In December 1942 a top-level meeting was held in the office of Sir John Fryer, Chief Scientist at the Ministry of Agriculture, attended by H G

Thornton and J H Quastel of Rothamsted, Lord Melchett (then ICI Chairman), Slade and Templeman. Frank Rayns, Director of the Norfolk Agricultural Station and a close friend of Sir John Fryer, was also present. Following this meeting, at which the implications of the Jealott's Hill and Rothamsted discoveries were discussed in detail, Rothamsted and Jealott's Hill pooled resources and P S Nutman of Rothamsted worked at Jealott's Hill with Templeman to set up further experiments with chemicals supplied by Sexton at Dyestuffs Division. This work identified as the most effective chemicals the sodium salts of MCPA and 2,4-D and discovered iso-propyl phenyl carbamate (IPC), of which more later. Field trials were carried out in the first instance in Norfolk under the aegis of Frank Rayns.

It must be remembered that these events took place at a time when, for security reasons, the results could not be published; in fact the ban on publicity was not lifted until 1945. Nonetheless, under the stimulus of wartime demand for food, attention was focused on the development of these chemicals, "with all deliberate speed," for the farmer. It was eventually decided that the sodium salt of MCPA should be developed, mainly because ICI had access to chlorocresol, one of the main intermediates in the manufacture of MCPA.

Up to this stage field work with MCPA and 2,4-D had been restricted and carried out in secret; field trials conducted away from Jealott's Hill had taken the form of small-plot trials hidden away in cereal fields on specially selected farms. It was now necessary to test MCPA on a much larger scale in cereal crops throughout the country. Accordingly, the largest programme of field trials ever attempted in the UK was launched under the direction of E Holmes, operating from Jealott's Hill. The programme embraced about 300 experimental centres chosen in co-operation with the War Agricultural Executive Committees, and covering a very wide range of weeds, soils and localities.

The trials were carried out by three mobile teams, each consisting of a biologist, an engineer and an agronomist. The teams travelled with all necessary application equipment mounted on a lorry and were capable of carrying out running repairs in the field. Each site was marked out, a weed census was taken and the chemical applied *as a dust* through a variety of fertilizer distributors. The centres were kept under observation throughout the season and yields were taken where possible.

The execution of this enormous programme had its humorous moments as when equipment got stuck in narrow lanes, when the fertilizer distributors proved too wide for farm gates, and when the suspicions of village policemen were aroused by the sinister appearance of the sheeted lorries; and more serious moments, happily infrequent, when a sudden change of wind direction carried MCPA dust into prized gardens.

I M Burnet, who was involved in the field demonstrational work, emphasises the point that every member of the experimental teams was well aware of the importance of the work and excited by the novelty of the project. There was a great competitive spirit between the teams, each striving to complete its full programme of trials. At first the task seemed impossible to accomplish but experience speeded up the work and it was completed very successfully—as Burnet says 'it was a great exercise carried out with good comradeship amongst all those concerned, and with a very satisfactory feeling of taking part in a great agricultural adventure' [1].

In 1946 MCPA was made available to UK farmers as a 1% dust, 'methoxone' or 'cornland cleaner', for application through fertilizer distributors. By this time reports had reached Jealott's Hill from the USA disclosing the development of spraying machinery capable of applying the growth regulator type of herbicide in small volumes of water as low as 4 to 6 gallons per acre. This was made possible through the use of nozzles similar to those used for air humidification, which gave a characteristically flat-fan shaped finely-divided spray providing economy in the use of water and labour and having good retention on the leaf surface.

W G Templeman [2] has described the work in some detail, indicating that experiments started at Jealott's Hill in 1947 with the object of constructing a cheap prototype boom-sprayer employing the North American principle and spray nozzles. It was, however, essential to find a British equivalent spray nozzle and this was eventually located in the Bray gas jet; this jet had a ceramic tip with a moulded abrasion-resistant orifice mounted in a threaded brass holder and was available in a variety of sizes, giving discharge rates at 30 lb/sq inch pressure ranging from 2 to 8 gallons per hour.

The nozzles were mounted on a boom and set to spray at 45° to the vertical from a height of 12 to 18 inches above the top of the crop (or ground). Early difficulties with nozzle blockage necessitated careful filtration, and this problem was eventually solved by putting the filter at the head of the spray tank so that both chemical and water were screeened as the tank was filled.

Field trials were carried out in 1948 involving 70 acres of cereals and grassland and using MCPA in 5 to 7 gallons of spray liquid per acre. Kill of broad-leaved weeds was very successful and demonstrated that the principle of low volume spraying was sound under UK conditions; the experience led quickly to a surge of interest by equipment manufacturers anxious to participate in the new spray technology.

Thus was born 'Agroxone' liquid, to be followed by 'Agroxone' Triple Strength which together heralded the widespread use of selective 'hormone'-type weedkillers in the UK.

During the period 1942–44 American workers, notably P C Marth and J W Mitchell, had also recognised the agricultural potential of substituted phenoxyacetic acids, in particular 2,4-D, and in 1944–45 both the British and American work on growth substances as selective herbicides was published [3, 4, 5].

As with the research reports, so publication of patent applications had not been possible during the war. Thus, ICI filed a UK patent application relating to both 2,4-D and MCPA on 7 April 1941, but the patent was not accepted and published until 13 December 1945. In the USA, the American Chemical Paint Company (subsequently renamed Amchem) filed an application for a US patent relating to 2,4-D and analogous halogenated phenoxy acids on 4 May 1945; this patent was issued on 11 December 1945 and, later, other manufacturers entered the field. By 1949 about 10,000 tons of 2,4-D were manufactured in the USA alone.

The search for new chemicals with increased activity or different selectivity led to fundamental studies on the mode of action of selective hormone weedkillers in many parts of the world. Measurements of uptake and movement of MCPA in plants were made at Jealott's Hill in the hope of discovering the basis for selective action. Adsorption studies were also carried out to investigate whether or not the chemicals were immobilised in resistant plants and, if so, how they could be released. The effect of MCPA on mitosis in plants was investigated, and yet other studies were concerned with the effect of MCPA on the mineral content, and particularly on the content of potassium ion, in treated plants.

These studies failed, however, to define the mechanism of selectivity of MCPA and 2,4-D; whilst they contributed to an increased understanding of the behaviour of the chemicals the exact mode of action remained unresolved.

Other derivatives of phenoxyacetic acid appeared later as a result of an empirical approach, and by workers outside ICI, largely in response to a need to control weed species which were proving resistant to MCPA and 2,4-D. Trichloro-derivatives, of which 2,4,5-trichlorophenoxyacetic and propionic acids are most well known, were found to control woody weed species. Still later, α-phenoxypropionic acids were introduced by the Boots Co Ltd. to control chickweed *(Stellaria media)* and cleavers *(Galium aparine)*. Selectivity was further extended by the introduction of β-phenoxybutyric acids. The latter are degraded selectively by different broad-leaved plants to toxic or non-toxic metabolites, and by their application it is possible, for example, to destroy weeds in cereal crops undersown with clover.

In retrospect, it is doubtful whether either ICI or Britain pursued the revolutionary discovery of the 'hormone' weedkillers with the zeal it merited; but there is no doubt that world agriculture benefited immensely, and that Jealott's Hill and W G Templeman in particular were instrumental in bringing about a significant and valuable change in farming practice.

Isopropylphenylcarbamate—IPC

In the screening tests for hormone weedkillers in 1940 workers at Jealott's Hill had discovered another group of chemicals—the phenylcarbamates —which were active in controlling plant growth. These compounds were also selective but the nature of the selectivity was different from that of the α-naphthyl- and phenoxyacetic acids. The carbamates controlled grass weeds in the presence of broad-leaved crops. Experiments showed that isopropyl N-phenylcarbamate, for example, prevented the growth of cereal seedlings but did not affect the growth of sugar beet, flax, rape and yellow charlock. Applied when the cereals were at an advanced growth stage, heavier applications of IPC were required but growth was still affected and, in these circumstances, although panicles and spikelets were formed, no grain developed.

Later studies showed that the timing of application was all-important. Autumn treatments were more effective than those made in the summer, although foliar sprays generally left much to be desired. Greater success attended treatments in which IPC was applied to the soil before crop emergence. IPC was used at 2·5 to 5·0 lb per acre alone and in mixture with MCPA. In 1948, experiments were conducted with pre-emergence applications to many crops such as kale, lettuce, onions, peas, lucerne, sugar beet and swedes with little or no damage to the crops but with good control of grasses and *Polygonum* species. Mixtures of IPC with MCPA were superior in action to either chemical applied singly, and weeds such as chickweed and cleavers, which are resistant to MCPA alone, were controlled satisfactorily by the mixture. The chemical was never developed extensively, however, and it was later superseded by its chloro- analogue (CIPC) which other workers found to be active against a wider range of grass weeds.

In common with many 'synthetic hormones' IPC had other growth regulating properties. Interest at Jealott's Hill in improving the storage of potatoes by chemical methods led to the discovery that IPC also inhibited the sprouting of potato tubers, an observation of considerable importance because premature sprouting reduces the weight and quality, and hence the market value, of the tubers.

In the spring of 1948 promising results emerged from preliminary experiments on potato tubers treated with IPC prior to storage the previous autumn. Small scale field trials conducted by L G Spencer confirmed these results in the spring of 1949, and the autumn of that year saw the initiation by D Price Jones, then at Fernhurst, of a programme of trials, most of which were on potatoes clamped under commercial conditions; a few consisted of treated potatoes stored in baskets or bags. Results were satisfactory, as were those of further trials the following year.

Assessments in the spring of 1951 indicated successful potato sprout suppression. Skin spot *(Oospora pustulans)* was noted in a few commercial clamps and in some Fernhurst trials but was insignificant and the value of the crop was not affected. Accordingly, following limited sales in 1950, IPC was marketed in July/August 1951 with the name 'Tuberite'.

Unfortunately, the late summer and autumn of 1951 were wet, and by the spring of 1952 there was a very high incidence of skin spot in commercial crops generally; but in 'Tuberite'-treated crops the disease penetrated tubers deeply and many of these damaged tubers were unsaleable.

It subsequently transpired that IPC, acting as a growth regulator, had slowed down the process whereby calluses form over wounds, and skin spot fungi were able to penetrate deeply into the cortex of the tubers, with very serious results.

Sales of 'Tuberite' in the UK were restricted severely in 1952 and ceased altogether by 1953, after which date the chemical was only sold as a sprout suppressant by Plant Protection Limited overseas where skin spot was not a problem. Nowadays, of course, CIPC and CIPC/IPC mixtures are widely used in the UK as potato sprout suppressants, but they are applied after the harvested tubers have had time to harden, or 'cure'.

References

[1] Burnet I M (1967) 'The MCPA story' *PANS* (C) **13** (2), 104–110

[2] Templeman W G (1949) 'Low volume sprayers for weed control' *Agriculture* **55,** 441–3

[3] Marth P C, Mitchell J W (1944) '2,4-dichlorophenoxyacetic acid as a differential herbicide' *Bot. Gaz.* **106,** 224–232

[4] Nutman P S, Thornton H G, Quastel J H (1945) 'Inhibition of plant growth by 2,4-dichlorophenoxyacetic acid and other plant growth substances' *Nature, Lond.* **155,** 498–500

[5] Slade R E, Templeman W G, Sexton W A (1945) 'Differential effects of plant growth substances on plant species'. *Nature, Lond.* **155,** 497–8

Chapter 5

Benzene hexachloride

Benzene hexachloride, more accurately described as hexachlorocyclohexane, was probably first made by Michael Faraday in 1825 by bubbling chlorine through benzene in sunlight, which gave what he described as 'a tenacious triple compound of chlorine, carbon and hydrogen'. George Ordish [1] points out that this procedure is substantially the same as that used today and that, contrary to some speculation, it is likely to have produced BHC. The early interest of ICI in this material is well recalled by C C Tanner, who was involved in the chemical work at Widnes Central Laboratory and later became Director of the Hawthorndale Laboratories at Jealott's Hill. In the 1930s there was interest, within the General Chemicals Division research department at Widnes, in chlorinated compounds for possible use as non-inflammable dielectric materials. One compound studied was trichlorobenzene, which was derived from benzene hexachloride, which was in turn made by reacting chlorine with benzene in ultraviolet light from a mercury vapour lamp.

The production of trichlorobenzene was troubled by an unreactive fraction of the BHC, which was identified as the beta isomer, everything else being thought, at that time, to be the alpha isomer. The isomeric nature of BHC was, of course, well known, having been investigated by van der Linden in 1912.

Samples of BHC were sent to Hawthorndale in the mid-1930s. The earliest record of any tests on BHC at Jealott's Hill appears to be in an internal report issued in March 1937 which records the results of a test for repellency to clothes moths. This was a multiple-choice type of test, in which the BHC-treated samples of cloth showed no repellent activity as measured by the numbers of moth eggs laid on the treated samples. It was noted, however, that all the adult moths were killed by exposure to the batch of test substances, any of which could have been responsible in this type of experiment. BHC, sample No. PC 135, next appears in work reported by F J D Thomas and G H Stock.

Issued in July 1942, this report gathers together the results of insecticide screening tests on some 75 different chemical samples, as part of a programme seeking possible substitutes for derris, imports of which were becoming difficult due to war conditions and the Japanese occupation of Malaya. Pesticide chemistry was then in its infancy, and there was a tendency for those at Widnes to regard the pesticide tests at Hawthorndale as a suitable destination for any intractable and evil-smelling residue for which no other use could be envisaged. Thomas remembered some of the earlier materials in this context and requested various samples from Widnes; BHC was included in the samples sent because, according to Tanner, 'there was a lot of it in the Widnes store'. Thomas and Stock included in their tests two different samples and five formulations of BHC as dusts or sprays. The test species were various caterpillars and aphids, together with locusts and red spider-mites. They were treated in the laboratory, on small potted plants or on detached shoots or leaves, by dusting with a hand dust-gun or by spraying with a hand-held atomiser spray. BHC killed high proportions of most of the insects in the test, and the report concludes that it 'possesses considerable toxicity to many species of aphids and caterpillars and also to locusts. Against red spider it appears less promising'.

Results of the initial screening tests had been made known to Plant Protection Ltd at Yalding, and a report by Ordish, also issued in July 1942, summarised a series of field experiments in Kent against raspberry beetle *(Byturus tomentosus)* and caterpillars on raspberry and cultivated blackberry, against flea beetles *(Phyllotreta* spp*)* on swedes and turnips and against aphids on hops, which fully confirmed the promise of the laboratory experiments.

The discovery of the insecticidal action of BHC by ICI was quite independent of any work on this material elsewhere, knowledge of which did not become available until later. The situation in relation to other work has been discussed by Ordish. The insecticidal activity of BHC was discovered in France in the early 1940s by A Dupire and M Raucourt in Paris, and Dupire took out a patent in 1941. J M Gomeza Ozámiz has also claimed independent discovery in Spain at around the same time, but did not publish until 1945. There is also a US patent filed in July 1933 by H Bender, whose work appears to have been concerned primarily with uses for chlorine. Bender chlorinated benzene in sunlight by adding benzene a little at a time to liquid chlorine, the operation being conducted, in the absence of suitable fume-cupboard space, in the middle of a field. He noted that the white crystalline product of this reaction killed flies and bees when left around exposed, and on this basis claimed insecticidal activity in the patent. In view of ICI's apparent failure to 'discover' BHC in 1937, it is interesting to note that a sample of Bender's product was sent to the University of California for testing as an insecticide, but produced a total lack of interest.

Through the summer of 1942, while the work of Thomas and Stock and of Ordish was proceeding, interest, even excitement, about BHC was clearly growing. J Clayton, who was working as a young assistant at Hawthorndale at the time, recalls this excitement, which was high-lighted by an incident in which a sample of the product sent from Widnes was sieved, on a Saturday morning, in a large room in Hawthorndale in which the culture of locusts was kept. On Monday morning all the locusts were found dead, and the cages remained toxic to locusts for a considerable time. Late in the summer of 1942, a deputation of chemists from Widnes, including Tanner, visited Hawthorndale to discuss plans, and arrangements were made for pure samples of the alpha and beta isomers of BHC—the only ones thought to be present in the crude material at that time—to be prepared and sent for testing. In due course the pure isomers were examined as insecticides against diamond-back moth (Plutella maculipennis) and small cabbage-white butterfly (Pieris brassicae) larvae. This work, reported by H R Jameson in October 1942, showed both the pure isomers to be relatively inactive in comparison with the crude product. The identification of the gamma isomer as the active compound did not occur until mid-1943. Such were the needs, however, for a substitute for the imported derris insecticide that plans for the large-scale production of crude BHC were initiated by Slade, the then ICI Research Controller, in the autumn of 1942, with a target of thirty tons by the spring of 1943 in time for the flea-beetle season. By the spring of 1943, however, the Widnes work on the isomeric constitution of crude BHC had shown that the material previously tested at Hawthorndale contained only 3–4% of the active isomer, since most of the gamma-BHC had been thrown out in the crystallisation clean-up process; and it was now found possible to produce material with around 12% of gamma isomer. Eventually, only about seven tons of the more active product had to be made to meet the projected need for thirty tons. Initially there was no suitable analytical method for use in quality control of the production process. A biological assay, based on the toxicity of the product to grain weevils (Sitophilus granarius) in jars of wheat, was devised by H H S Bovingdon, and from 1943 a long series of internal reports records 'determination of the active ingredient in 666'. The sobriquet '666' competed with 'BHC' for some time, no doubt from recognition of its potential value as a highly individual trade name, but it gradually disappeared with the growth of interest in the gamma isomer, for which Slade later coined the name 'Gammexane'.

BHC was initially formulated as a dust containing 20% of the crude material with gypsum as a diluent, and from 1943 onwards it was deployed against a wide range of insect pests. At Hawthorndale, extensive work on locusts indicated a spectacular activity and led to the communication of the results to B P Uvarov, then Director of the Anti-Locust Research Centre under the Colonial Office in London. As a result of this, field trials were arranged in North Africa, with highly successful results. In wartime conditions in the UK, the most pressing pest problems were wireworms (Agriotes spp) in cereals and potatoes, particularly in the large areas of permanent grassland newly ploughed for arable use, and flea beetles on brassicas. These agricultural uses were investigated by Jameson [2, 3, 4], while Bovingdon started work on the control of stored-product pests and flies.

In the early wireworm trials in 1943 it was found that combine-drilling 1 cwt/ac of a 2% BHC dust controlled the past and gave a five-fold increase in yield of oats and wheat. In the presence of the massive wireworm populations which then existed, even greater yield increases were possible as, for example, occurred on winter wheat at Windsor in 1945–46, when the yield on the control plot was only 3 cwt per acre, compared with 23 cwt per acre where a BHC seed treatment was used. Trials in 1944–45 had compared a seed treatment with granules and dust treatments in the drill-row, and had shown that a seed treatment with 8% gamma-BHC powder at 5 oz/bushel (equivalent to 0·1 lb of gamma-BHC per acre or 0·11 kg/ha) gave a five-fold increase in the yield of oats. At the end of 1945 gamma-BHC of 98% purity became available and trials showed that a 20% gamma-BHC formulation applied at 0·04% gamma-BHC on the weight of the seed (equivalent to 0·08 lb gamma-BHC per acre) gave the same yield increase as 1·0 cwt of a 2% BHC dust combine drilled (equivalent to 0·27 lb gamma-BHC) per acre.

A field trials programme which began in 1946 examined the effect of combined seed treatments containing 1% mercury, mainly as phenyl mercury acetate, but with a little ethyl mercury chloride, and a range of gamma-BHC concentrations. Between 1946 and 1948 Jameson and F C Peacock showed that there was a linear increase in yield of 0·75 to 1·0 cwt per acre (94–125 kg/ha) for every 5% increase in the gamma-BHC content in the formulation when wireworm attack was moderate to heavy, but delayed germination and plant damage were found at the highest concentrations of BHC. The commercial product based on these findings was launched in 1949 with the name 'Mergamma' A, and contained 1% mercury and 20% gamma-BHC; it was recommended for use at 2 oz per bushel, giving 22 ppm mercury and 440 ppm gamma-BHC on the seed. This product was followed by a series of other 'Mergamma' formulations for specialised uses on particular crops, and dual-purpose seed treatments thereafter developed widely in various parts of the world where soil pests were a problem. Because, for a variety of reasons, gamma-BHC is less environmentally undesirable than many chlorinated hydrocarbon compounds it has continued to be used long after compounds such as aldrin, dieldrin and heptachlor were banned in many countries.

The use of BHC against pests on top fruit was developed between 1948 and 1950 by J H Stapley, working from Plant Protection Ltd's centre at Fernhurst. This range of pests had been conventionally controlled by the use of tar oil or DNC/oil sprays during the dormant season, followed by the use of lead arsenate and derris during the summer, with DDT providing convenient and highly effective control of apple blossom weevil (*Anthonomus pomorum*). Stapley concentrated on the development of a BHC programme, using a dispersible powder formulation of crude BHC. The programme devised involved four spray applications, starting at bud-burst, and successfully controlled apple blossom weevil, caterpillars, aphids, suckers, capsids, woolly aphids (*Eriosoma lanigerum*) and apple sawfly (*Hoplocampa testudinea*).

By 1944, however, it had become apparent that BHC could cause a musty flavour in certain foods after treatment of the crop in the field. This taint was particularly pronounced in potatoes and some other root crops; no taint problems arose with top fruit, but black currants were particularly susceptible. Investigations on taint were started by Jameson in 1944 and over the next few years the tasting panel was a feature of life for those who worked at Hawthorndale. Each mid-morning and mid-afternoon a handbell was rung from the 'taint kitchen' and all those present in the building would assemble to taste the offerings on randomly-arranged numbered plates. Mashed potato figured largely on the menu, but also included were swede, carrot (both particularly unpleasant when tainted), onion, beet, various fruits, chicken, eggs and even potato chips fried in fat derived from chickens fed on treated grain. Severe taint was associated with the use of crude BHC, but it was eventually shown that even pure gamma-BHC could produce taint in certain particularly susceptible crops. In practice, the greatest problem was posed by potatoes which, grown on land treated with BHC for a preceding crop, were liable to be tainted for some years afterwards.

The exploitation of BHC in the public health field, particularly in malaria control, undoubtedly suffered by the prior development of DDT. Crude BHC had a particularly pervasive smell, and in laboratory experiments on non-porous surfaces such as glass plates, it was markedly less persistent than DDT. In practice, in the primitive social conditions in which much malaria control was carried out, the smell was often not as aggressive as others naturally present; and, on the surfaces to be treated, such as mud, brick and plaster, persistence was little different from that of DDT, as was shown later in work by F S Downing and others in East Africa.

Insecticide smoke dispersal, for which the pyrotechnic expertise of ICI's Explosives (now Nobel) Division at Ardeer in Scotland was co-opted, was one of the more colourful aspects of the development of BHC. Some of the early smoke-generating compositions were somewhat uncertain in their burning characteristics and it was felt that the biological testing would be more prudently carried out in an explosives facility. Biological assay of the performance of the smoke generators was done by exposing glass plates and fibre-board squares to the smoke and then allowing grain weevils and flour beetles to walk over them. As confidence in the life expectancy of experimenters grew, the later biological evaluation of smokes was transferred to Jealott's Hill. Various BHC smoke compositions were produced for disinfestation of food stores and led to later work on the dispersal of organophosphate and other pesticides in glasshouses.

In the autumn of 1950, J F Newman was seconded to the Rockefeller Foundation to work on the malaria eradication project in Sardinia. It was at this time that the problem of the acquired resistance of pests to the organochlorine pesticides was becoming apparent. The Sardinian campaign, ultimately successful in eliminating malaria transmission in the island, also drew attention to the way in which some insects, notably houseflies, could become resistant to pesticides. Resistance developed initially to DDT, but it was found that there was some measure of cross-resistance to other compounds, so that BHC and other organochlorine compounds became progressively less effective when they were used in place of DDT. Samples of BHC-resistant flies were brought back to Jealott's Hill and studies on the acquisition of organochlorine resistance began. It was found that, whereas a susceptible laboratory population failed under BHC pressure to develop resistance through some 20 generations, due no doubt to absence of the necessary genetic characteristics, it was possible, by selection with increasing quantities of BHC, to build up resistance in the Sardinian resistant strain to very high levels [5]. Radiochemical techniques, using ^{14}C labelled gamma-BHC, were developed by F R Bradbury at General Chemicals Division, and were used to investigate the uptake and metabolism of BHC in resistant and susceptible strains of flies [6].

Up to this time little had been done to investigate the physiological mode of action of BHC. Slade, in his early publication on BHC [7], had suggested that, on the basis of postulated stereochemical similarity, BHC might interfere in the metabolism of inositol and block some vital function in the insect. It was later shown, however, that inositol did not resemble the active gamma isomer. At Jealott's Hill, neurophysiological experiments were devised to investigate effects on neuromuscular junctions, central nervous synapses and sensory and motor axonic transmission in the locust. This work, initiated by Newman, and developed by Ann Harlow [8] and H S Hopf, was soon diverted to the study of the rapidly developing organophosphorus insecticides, but enough had been done to show that the action of BHC was somewhat differently localised from that of DDT.

Whilst the crop protection uses of gamma BHC described here, and its development in the control of cocoa capsids in West Africa, referred to in a later chapter, were exploited by ICI through Plant Protection Limited, uses in the veterinary field against lice, ticks, mites and blowflies were, by agreement, left to Cooper, McDougall & Robertson.

Public health outlets were 'nobody's child' and largely ignored; malaria, tsetse-fly and locust control studies with BHC were carried out by bodies such as the World Health Organisation, United Nations Relief & Rehabilitation Administration, The Food and Agriculture Organisation of the United Nations and the Anti-Locust Research Centre. As such they fall outside the scope of this book, regrettably, since it is now difficult to find an account of the benefits to mankind which resulted from such applications.

Looking back, it is evident that BHC represented the end of the age of simplicity in crop protection, for ICI as for everyone else, producer and consumer. 'Discovered' in 1942, in widespread use by 1946, BHC's development costs were ludicrously small by present-day standards. The wholly laudatory introduction of checks to the use of new chemicals in the agriculture of developed countries, by their adoption world-wide placed such materials, for better or for worse, ever further beyond the reach of the subsistence farmer in 'Third-world' countries, where priorities may well be different.

References

[1] Ordish G (1976) *The constant pest,* Peter Davies, London. pp 240
[2] Jameson H R (1958) 'The mechanism of control of turnip flea beetle by benzene hexachloride dressings on brassica seed' *J. Sci. Fd Agric.* **9**, 590–596

[3] Jameson H R, Thomas F J D, Woodward R C (1947) 'The practical control of wireworm with gamma BHC: comparison with DDT' *Ann. appl. Biol.* **34,** 346–56

[4] Jameson H R, Thomas F J D, Tanner C C (1951) 'The control of wireworm by gamma BHC. The development of a seed dressing for cereals' *Ann. appl. Biol.* **38,** 121–34

[5] Newman J F (1957) 'Resistance to insecticides' *Outl. Agric.* **1,** 235–239

[6] Bradbury F R, Nield P, Newman J F (1953) 'Amount of gamma- BHC picked up by resistant houseflies bred on a medium containing benzene hexachloride' *Nature, Lond.* **172,** 1052

[7] Slade R E (1945) 'The gamma isomer of hexachlorocyclohexane ('Gammexane')' The Hurter Memorial Lecture to the Society of Chemical Industry. *Chemy. Ind.* **40,** 314–319

[8] Harlow P Ann (1958) 'The action of drugs on the nervous system of the locust *(Locusta migratoria)*' *Ann. appl. Biol.* **46** (1) 55–73

3
MCPA
4

1 Selective weedkilling 1937,
  spraying sulphuric acid
2 Control of charlock in spring oats
  with MCPA, 1950s
3 Low-volume spray rig, 1947

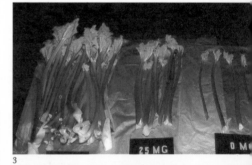

1 GA on pruned tea, Indonesia:
  centre rows treated
2 GA on capsicums, Sicily: centre
  rows treated
3 GA on forced rhubarb: left to
  right – 100 mg 'Berelex' per
  crown; 25 mg 'Berelex';
  untreated
4 GA on seedless grapes to
  increase berry size: left
  untreated; right 20 ppm GA

Chapter 6

Organophosphorus insecticides

Although organic phosphorus compounds such as tetraethyl pyrophosphate (TEPP) had been known since the middle of the last century it was not until immediately before World War II that a vigorous interest was shown in their chemistry, largely due to the pioneer work of G Schrader in the 1930s at IG Farbenfabriken Bayer in Germany. It appears that Schrader's interest in organophosphorus compounds as potential insecticides was first aroused by the activity of diethylfluorophosphonate which, by his own account, was arrived at by a step-by-step process of reasoning starting from the known effect of methane sulphonyl fluoride as a fumigating insecticide against grain weevil. It might equally well have arisen during the course of chemical warfare research, as did the corresponding di-isopropyl-fluorophosphonate in work by a group at Cambridge headed by B C Saunders. The German workers, however, paid special attention to the insecticidal properties of the substances and, by the end of the war, had made many active molecules including TEPP, dimefox, schradan and parathion. This information came to light with the publication in 1947 of three British Intelligence Objectives Sub-Committee reports, and considerable interest was aroused in parathion (E605) which was later manufactured by Albright & Wilson for Plant Protection Ltd.

The potential for further insecticide discoveries of this nature was reviewed in 1948 by a joint ICI Dyestuffs/General Chemicals Division Pest Control Research Committee which concluded that the discoveries already made in Germany had 'closed the remaining gap in the insecticide field' (!). Entomologists at Jealott's Hill and some chemists, however, argued strongly that there was still ample scope for further products among the organophosphates and, as a result of their arguments, Dyestuffs Division instructed one chemist, R Ghosh, to carry out speculative work in this area of chemistry.

Most of the compounds discovered up to this time were quite toxic to mammals (oral LD_{50} to rat ranging from 1 to 20 mg/kg) and their toxicity had been shown to be related to powerful inhibition of acetylcholinesterase

(CHE), an important enzyme involved in the transmission of nerve impulses. It was not known whether or not their insecticidal activity was due to this property, but it was a reasonable premise on which to proceed. Early in 1952 Ghosh prepared S-2-(diethylamino) ethyl 0,0-diethyl phosphorothiolate, as the hydrogen oxalate salt (amiton; later given the trade name 'Tetram' **II**), which was an organophosphorus analogue of the natural substrate acetylcholine (**I**).

$$\overset{\overset{\text{O}}{\|}}{\text{CH}_3\text{COCH}_2\text{CH}_2\overset{+}{\text{N}}(\text{CH}_3)_3}$$

I   acetylcholine

$$(\text{C}_2\text{H}_5\text{O})_2\overset{\overset{\text{O}}{\|}}{\text{P}}\text{SCH}_2\text{CH}_2\text{N}(\text{C}_2\text{H}_5)_2,(\text{COOH})_2$$

II   amiton

$$(\text{CH}_3\text{O})_2\overset{\overset{\text{S}}{\|}}{\text{P}}\text{SCH}_2$$

III   menazon

Amiton was tested at Jealott's Hill where it was shown to possess remarkable variation in toxicity to different groups of insects and spider mites [1]. It was much less toxic than parathion to the major insect groups but was at least seven times more toxic to the glasshouse spider-mite *(Tetranychus telarius)*. Field trials during 1953 and 1954 demonstrated the high acaricidal activity of amiton against the fruit-tree red spider-mite *(Panonychus ulmi)*. It was shown to be absorbed rapidly by the foliage and gave almost season-length control of mites from a single application at a spray concentration of 20 ppm.

Interest in this compound and its close analogues was intense both at Jealott's Hill and at the Industrial Hygiene Research Laboratories, then located at Welwyn in Hertfordshire. J C Gage, at IHRL, showed that these compounds were powerful mammalian acetylcholinesterase inhibitors both *in vitro* and *in vivo*. The oral LD_{50} of amiton to the rat was about 5 mg/kg. The thionate analogue of amiton was shown to be a much weaker CHE inhibitor [2], which supported the earlier researches of Gage [3], who had demonstrated that the strong CHE-inhibitory action of parathion was due to conversion in the body to its oxygen analogue, paraoxon.

Meanwhile, insect physiology studies by H S Hopf, J F Newman and Ann Harlow at Jealott's Hill were throwing further light on the selective toxicity of amiton. Experiments using fly brain homogenates and cockroach ganglia, and with locust legs stimulated to kick traces on a revolving cylinder of smoked paper, demonstrated that amiton was a potent inhibitor of insect cholinesterase. The relatively low toxicity to most insect species *in vivo* was explained by the slow penetration of the insect nerve sheath by the ionised molecule. Penetration to the insect ganglion was shown to be ten to fifteen times slower for ionised substances compared with neutral molecules such as parathion. The central nervous system of mammals, although similarly protected, is more sensitive to charged molecules by virtue of its unprotected peripheral system. This inverse selectivity, to the disadvantage of vertebrates, was shown to be even more pronounced in the case of quaternary salts of the original basic phosphorus ester. Thus the LD_{50} of the ethyl iodide quaternary salt was shown to be around 750 mg/kg in locusts and about 0·1 mg/kg in rats.

Development work against spider mites in UK orchards, on cotton in Egypt and on citrus and other crops in the USA, by E C Edgar and F L Baranyovits at Jealott's Hill and J Robson at Fernhurst, confirmed the high activity and long persistence of amiton in the field. However, the routine medical examination of spray operators disclosed severe blood-CHE-level depression in several individuals and, although medical opinion on the significance of such depression in the human system varied, it became clear that the product could not responsibly be marketed. The decision was rapidly taken to abandon any further development, though not without regret. Amiton is probably still the most active compound against spider-mites ever discovered. One farmer found spraying the chemical without any protective clothing, and warned that he could kill himself, was so alarmed that he asked for the remaining product to be removed from his farm. Later, having seen his trees clear of spider-mites throughout the summer, he asked for a further supply! Although the selective toxicity of the compound to insects and mammals can be readily explained from the work at Jealott's Hill and elsewhere, its high toxicity to mites remains a mystery.

The discovery of amiton, though commercially unsuccessful, encouraged increased synthetic effort on organophosphorus compounds at Dyestuffs Division, with the object of trying to find an insecticide which was much less toxic to mammals than existing products. The chances of success were not rated very high at the time by one prominent ICI consultant, and it was true that when selectivity had occurred it had been invariably to the disadvantage of mammals. However, 'where ignorance is bliss, 'tis folly to be wise'; and in the organophosphorus insecticide field in the mid-1950s this brand of ignorance produced American Cyanamid's malathion and ICI's menazon, both compounds of exceptionally low toxicity to mammals. The acute oral LD_{50} of malathion to rats was 2,800 mg/kg, whilst the compound showed good insecticidal activity. It is now known that the high degree of selective toxicity exhibited by this compound is due to the relative rates of oxidation, $P=S \rightarrow P=O$ (activation) and hydrolysis (detoxification). The latter is the predominant process in mammalian liver whilst oxidation is the major process in insect tissue.

In 1955 a group of chemists was transferred from Dyestuffs Division, Manchester, to Jealott's Hill to continue the synthesis of potential crop protection chemicals, and to maintain closer liaison and co-operation with biologists already working there. Despite the growing importance of the bipyridylium herbicides at Jealott's Hill, effort was maintained in the organophosphorus insecticide field, with low mammalian toxicity as a primary objective.

The first, perhaps rather naive, approach was to elaborate on the amiton model by maintaining the two-carbon chain between a nitrogen atom and a phosphorus ester group, but reducing the basic character of the molecule. Among the first few compounds synthesised at Jealott's Hill were a phosphorylated acetamide and a phosphorylated aminotriazine which displayed outstanding activity in the insecticide screen. The oral LD_{50} to rats of these compounds was in the range 20–50 mg/kg, not a great improvement on parathion. Whilst the amide showed general insecticidal activity the aminotriazine was highly selective against aphids while exhibiting little toxicity to other insect groups. Major interest centred on this selectivity to aphids [4] and, as a result of further refinement of the molecule (changing $P=O$ to $P=S$ and diethyl to the dimethyl ester), the mammalian toxicity was reduced by a factor of about one hundred-fold with no loss of aphicidal activity.

The resulting compound (**III,** page 50), subsequently named menazon and marketed under the trade name 'Sayfos', had an oral LD_{50} to the rat of almost 2000 mg/kg. It was shown to possess very high contact, residual and systemic toxicity to aphids but it had relatively little effect on other insect species [4]. Thus, it was approximately five times more toxic than parathion to the pea aphid *(Macrosiphum pisum)*, whilst it was one thousand times less toxic than parathion to larvae of the mosquito *(Aedes aegypti).*

It is interesting to reflect that similar chemical modifications of the amide might have resulted in dimethoate, which has an oral LD_{50} to the rat of 350 mg/kg; however, Montecatini patents claiming this compound were published at about this time.

More detailed glasshouse and laboratory studies with menazon, followed by field trials in the UK and continental Europe, confirmed its value as a selective aphicide on a wide range of fruit and vegetable crops. Experiments with ^{32}P- and ^{14}C-radio-labelled menazon had earlier shown that the compound was systemic and readily absorbed by plant roots and translocated throughout the plant. Transport, however, was essentially upwards in the xylem. It was poorly translocated in the phloem, so that movement of the chemical was limited following a foliar spray, though important translaminar activity was demonstrated; thus, application of the chemical to the upper surface of plant leaves killed aphids feeding on the underside. It could be used as a seed-dressing or soil drench giving protection of the plant during the early stages of growth—important for the control of aphid-borne plant virus diseases—and it was non-phytotoxic at the dose levels needed for aphid control, even to the young roots of germinating potato tubers, seeds and transplants.

Chemical analysis of treated plants showed also that menazon was highly persistent when applied as a foliage spray or as a seed dressing. This was surprising for an organophosphorus compound, but it accounted for field results which showed that biological effects could persist for many weeks after application.

Considerable interest centred round its use as a seed-dressing for sugar beet to control aphids and the spread of virus yellows. J A W Turner and L G Spencer at Jealott's Hill, and R A Dunning, at Broom's Barn Experimental Station in Suffolk, carried out trials over several years in the UK and established that 'Saphizon'—a seed dressing dispersible powder formulation of menazon—would control aphids virtually completely up to the end of May and partially into July, with a corresponding decrease in the incidence of early virus yellows. Plant Protection trials in northern and central Europe confirmed its value in this application but results were variable and were dependent on soil moisture, the amount of rainfall and the period at which aphid infestation occurred. Marketed as 'Sayfos', a dispersible powder formulation which could be used as a seed dressing or foliar spray, menazon was recommended as an aphicide on potatoes, sugar beet, beans, brassicas, soft fruit, apples and other crops, where it gave protection for long periods, and it found favour particularly in Eastern Europe, Japan and India where safety and/or persistence of effects are primary considerations. And because of its safety, the product 'Abol X' was developed specifically for the home gardener. But its commercial development as a foliar spray was marred by its complete lack of fumigant action, which is particularly important for aphid control under hot dry conditions on plants and trees with dense foliage which is difficult to penetrate and wet.

In many ways menazon was before its time. It showed high selectivity in controlling only the target species and was harmless to beneficial insects such as predators and pollinating insects. Furthermore, it was completely safe to the applicator, or farmer, and was apparently without any environmental problems. It was probably one of the first organophosphorus insecticides to have its metabolism in plants studied using ^{14}C-labelled material—an essential requirement of registration authorities in many countries today. It was shown to be degraded slowly in plants to non-toxic hydrolysis products.

The aphicidal mode of action of menazon presented a particularly interesting problem; both it and the $P=O$ form are very poor cholinesterase inhibitors *in vitro* and it became necessary to assume that activation to a more toxic metabolite occurred either in the plant or in the susceptible species (aphids). There were several arguments against activation in the plant. Plant metabolism studies using ^{14}C-, ^{32}P- and ^{35}S-labelled menazon yielded only hydrolysis products; no evidence of a more potent CHE-inhibiting derivative that could account for the aphicidal activity was found. Other species (e.g. soft brown scale insects) feeding on the vascular system of plants were not affected; and finally, menazon was aphicidal by contact application.

Some evidence for the second possibility was obtained. By harvesting freshly-fallen aphids from a broad bean plant treated with ^{32}P- and ^{14}C-labelled menazon the amount of radioactivity in the aphids was found to be approximately 1 mg/kg. The corresponding amount of radioactivity found in aphids from a schradan-treated plant was 15–20 mg/kg, yet schradan is a very much more potent CHE inhibitor. Also, it appeared that *in vitro* CHE activity was increased after administration of menazon to aphids. These experiments suggest that menazon was acting as, perhaps, the ideal pest control agent: one which is rendered active only by the species against which it is aimed, by a lethal synthesis akin to the selective effect of the so-called 'hormone' weedkillers. Regrettably, all attempts to isolate and characterise this active metabolite failed.

Subsequent work at Jealott's Hill on organophosphorus and carbamate insecticides forms the subject of a later chapter.

References

[1] Ghosh R, Newman J F (1955) 'A new group of organo-phosphorus pesticides' *Chemy Ind.* 118

[2] Calderbank A, Ghosh R (1960) 'The preparation and isomerization of some basic esters of *0,0-* diethyl hydrogen phosphorothionate' *J Chem. Soc.* **131,** 637

[3] Gage J C (1953) 'A cholinesterase inhibitor derived from *0,0-*diethyl *0-p*-nitrophenyl thiophosphate *in vivo' Biochem. J.* **54,** 426–30

[4] Calderbank A, Edgar E C, Silk J A (1961) 'Triazinyl thiophosphate esters with selective aphicidal properties' *Chemy Ind.* 630–631

Chapter 7

The gibberellins

Plant growth regulator research at Jealott's Hill in the 1930s brought together W G Templeman and W A Sexton, a chemist working with ICI Dyestuffs Division. ICI's interest in the gibberellins stems from this association, for it was in 1950 that Sexton, by then Research Director of ICI's Pharmaceuticals Division, first drew the Company's attention to the literature on these chemicals. They were reported in work from Japan, which by 1939 had succeeded in isolating small quantities of impure material, with powerful plant growth-promoting activity, from the fungus *Gibberella fujikuroi*, a pathogen of rice.

The Japanese work had gone unrecognised during World War II, and it was not until 1952 that ICI began to follow it up. Work then began in the Akers Research Laboratories at Welwyn and shortly after, as the hormone began to become available, at Jealott's Hill.

At Welwyn, P W Brian's team of biologists and the Akers chemists isolated a pure gibberellin, gibberellin A_3 or gibberellic acid (GA), and went on to propose its chemical structure [1]; other members of the team, notably G W Elson, H G Hemming and Margaret Radley, began to explore the physiology of gibberellins in higher plants, demonstrating their basic properties and their interaction with auxin. Such developments and the use of bioassay systems during these studies led to the discovery that natural hormones with physiological properties very similar to GA were widely distributed in higher plants. Confirmation that these natural hormones were indeed gibberellins was later provided by the isolation of pure gibberellins from runner bean seeds by J McMillan and J Suter of the same group. Simultaneously A Borrow, E G Jefferies and others were developing methods of culturing *Gibberella* to produce GA in considerably greater yields than had previously been possible. This important part of the Akers Laboratories work, coupled with the early isolation work of P J Curtis, provided the basis for some of the more important ICI patents.

Furthermore, it made 100-gram quantities of GA available to Jealott's Hill, and enabled work to begin on the search for agricultural uses.

At Jealott's Hill it was natural to examine the effect of GA on the productivity of pastures, grassland management having been a major interest of the research station since its inception. Furthermore, it was an interest fitting well with what was known in the early 1950s of the physiological activities of GA. The most obvious effect, that had originally attracted the Japanese workers to study the rice pathogen, was its ability to increase vegetative growth dramatically. In dicotyledons the stem length was increased, while in many monocotyledons the leaves also became longer; as leaves were the organs mainly cropped in pastures it was hoped that GA would directly increase yields. The field work was carried out by D G Morgan and G C Mees, assisted by L G Spencer and others on ICI's grassland farms.

The principal conclusion of this study was that GA could indeed promote grass growth in the field. In various experiments the dry-matter production at the first cut following treatment was increased by 0·6 to 10·8 cwt/acre (75–1350 kg/ha), with a small reduction in the protein content of the grass. If, however, the grass was allowed to regrow after cutting without further treatment, yields at the next cut were reduced, and there was no overall improvement. The only discernible advantage of GA treatment was to make the pastures productive early in the spring when climatic conditions were adverse and when fertilizers applied alone were relatively ineffective.

The production of grass in early spring, although of some value because of the high cost of feed at this time, was clearly not going to pay for the high cost of a chemical produced by a fermentation process. Furthermore, the complexity of the molecule made synthesis look impossible. The experimental work by Jealott's Hill staff was therefore wound up in 1956 after experiments on cereals and various horticultural crops had also failed to demonstrate how the effects on vegetative growth could be turned into economic increases in yields.

The cessation of work happened to coincide with an explosion of interest in gibberellins in a much wider scientific circle; an interest also taken up by the popular press. The effects on plant growth were undoubtedly spectacular, and some popular accounts made euphoric predictions of a revolution in agriculture led by GA. Thus, viewed in retrospect, the decision made at Jealott's Hill in 1956 may appear to have been premature, but it should be seen against the background of the then relatively small size of the establishment and its heavy commitment to development of the bipyridyls, the subject of a later chapter. In the event, the subsequent history of GA has largely supported the early Jealott's Hill opinion, at least insofar as the promotion of vegetative growth is concerned. But the chemical has a variety of other physiological activities, and it was some of these that were to prove more readily exploitable.

In 1956 P W Brian and Margaret Radley at Akers Laboratories patented the discovery that the malting of barley could be accelerated by the addition of minute amounts of GA prior to germination. This observation stimulated considerable interest by E Sandegren, H Beling and others in malting industry research circles which, by July 1959, led to the decision to develop this use. Plant Protection Ltd undertook the technical and commercial development with F P Coyne of the Technical Service Department responsible for co-ordination, joined later by J N Turner. Manufacture became a matter for ICI Pharmaceuticals Division at their penicillin plant in Trafford Park, Manchester.

In the meantime work elsewhere was beginning to indicate possibilities of practical use in agriculture unconnected with the stimulation of vegetative growth. Thus, R J Weaver and co-workers in California had demonstrated that when GA was applied to seedless grapes during fruit set, fruit size was greatly increased. R E Coggins and H Z Hield, also in California, were working on an interesting ability of GA to delay the ageing and associated physiological degeneration of the skin of some citrus fruits. L T Blaney and others in Oregon had demonstrated the ability of GA to increase the fruit set of some varieties of pear.

As much of this work was taking place in the USA it is not surprising that parts of the American fermentation industry became interested in acquiring licences to manufacture, develop and sell GA in the USA. Influenced no doubt by the still very considerable uncertainties clouding the future of the product in agriculture, and PPL's fully committed development resources, ICI granted licences to five US companies. In fact only four of these, Abbott Laboratories, Merck & Co. Inc., Eli Lilly & Co. and Pfizer Inc. took up their options to manufacture. In Japan, Takeda Chemical Industries were granted a similar licence.

Development of the malting use proceeded rapidly in the UK and subsequently in Western Europe and Australia. In the USA the licensees, all then primarily pharmaceutical companies with, at best, limited agro-chemical research facilities, furthered the development of the product largely by sponsoring appropriate University research groups. This policy, making use of the excellent University-linked Extension Services, got early acceptance for GA by the majority of Californian growers of seedless table grapes, followed by the development of a use in navel oranges and lemons where delayed ripening enabled growers to avoid low prices during market gluts. A further use in citrus emerged from work by A H Krezdorn at the University of Florida, who demonstrated that the Orlando tangelo, a variety of mandarin, could be induced to set fruit without pollination by timely application of GA.

By the early 1960s applied research interest was intense, with experiments in a large number of crops, often of an uncritical nature, taking little account of careful timing and other factors necessary for success. Even pigs and poultry were not immune, with never-to-be-confirmed claims of increased growth rates appearing in the scientific literature.

With development of the malting outlet proceeding satisfactorily, Plant Protection Ltd, for its part, was able to devote increasing attention to the introduction of the developing American techniques into other parts of the world and to seeking ways of exploiting the many published research leads. With the retirement of F P Coyne this work was co-ordinated by J N Turner and later G W Elson. It was progressed by various means, sometimes, as in the USA, through Universities and Extension Services, and sometimes through PPL's overseas organisation and agents.

As a result, the Californian grape treatment was modified to suit the widely-differing requirements of Greece and Turkey, Egypt and South Africa, Australia and Iran; the early pear-set observations found ready application to the frost-damaged blossom of some UK and Western European pear varieties; and the Orlando tangelo work was adapted to suit the clementines of Israel, Spain and Morocco. When Italian and Israeli research workers demonstrated that the cropping of globe artichokes could be advanced, often by as much as two or three months, techniques were developed to suit the commercial requirements of these and other countries, a matter of difficulty because widely-differing dose rates and timings were needed on different varieties.

Elsewhere the observation of D T Tomkins at Washington State University, that GA could largely replace the chilling required to break rhubarb dormancy, was to prove valuable to the early rhubarb growers of Holland, Canada and the UK. In Canada it was found that the serious depression of sour cherry yields resulting from growth inhibition caused by cherry yellow virus could be reversed, and normal cropping restored, by annual GA treatment. In sub-tropical regions a use was developed for the treatment of freshly-harvested potatoes, to break dormancy before replanting as seed for the second annual crop.

Many other small and very varied outlets have since been developed. Watercress beds are treated to maintain quality during the short days of winter. Application to seedless hops increases yields. Treatment of some ornamentals increases stem length and cut-flower quality. Post-harvest treatment of limes preserves their greenness and so extends their shipping range. These are but a few examples of the many small uses which contribute to the present world utilisation of about six tonnes of GA per annum—small by normal agrochemical standards but more readily appreciated when allowance is made for the high activity of the chemical. Rates as low as 5 gm/ha are effective in some instances.

For every successful use that has been developed there have been many failures and, most significantly, no use has yet been found that is capable of exploitation in a major field or plantation crop in spite of years of effort by ICI Plant Protection and others in sugarcane, oil palm, tropical pasture grasses, tea, cotton and other fibre crops. Sometimes in low-value crops the constraint has been economic. Sometimes, although technically and economically-viable treatments have been identified, the potential users are insufficiently advanced and flexible in their farm management methods to utilise the benefits fully. More often, however, technical difficulties are the barrier. On occasion, the timing of treatment has to be impractically precise. In other instances, major differences in the response of varieties within a species create problems, or relatively small differences in climatic conditions can thwart practical use. Perhaps the greatest problem has been the undeveloped state of the science of plant growth regulation, in which an appreciation of the complex inter-relationships between the natural growth regulators is only just beginning; the development of this knowledge may at last permit a departure from a largely empirical approach to the practical exploitation of exogenously-applied chemicals.

The present attitude of Jealott's Hill to the development of uses for the gibberellins and other growth regulators is very different from the 'spray it and see' techniques that seemed so reasonable in the early 1950s. More emphasis is put on getting a correct hormone balance, and minor or inconsistent responses obtained with GA alone sometimes become highly significant when other growth regulators are applied at the same time or used in sequence. Knowledge of the factors influencing the movement of growth-regulating chemicals within the plant is put to use, and advances in formulation chemistry or spraying technology are sometimes capable of greatly reducing the cost of a treatment.

Jealott's Hill research has also contributed to the discovery of practical uses for two of the other forty-five known gibberellins in addition to GA. These are gibberellins A_4 and A_7, at present produced as a mixture for reasons of economy. A_4/A_7 treatment will retard the premature ripening of bananas during shipment and greatly improve the efficacy of the fungicides used to prevent spoilage by crown rot. In Canada, R P Pharis has demonstrated that A_4/A_7 in admixture with A_3 and the indole auxin analogues will increase seed production in the otherwise sparsely-bearing Douglas fir seed nurseries. Similar constraints apply in other parts of the world and forestry research workers are obtaining encouraging results using Pharis's technique on other species of forest trees. Possibly of even greater long-term benefit to world timber production is the demonstrated ability of gibberellins to induce flowering and fruiting in some important conifers within the first year of growth instead of the more normal 6 to 10 years. Thus, for the first time, the application of the techniques of plant breeding to forest trees has become a practical proposition.

Finally, it is of interest to look at commercial policies for the gibberellins. Throughout the 17 years of GA manufacture these have been greatly influenced by the original decision to license manufacturers in the USA. In the early years of development this operated very much to the advantage of ICI; the sponsorship of research and development by the US licensees undoubtedly resulted in the reasonably rapid development of the sophisticated American horticultural outlets, and this in turn made a considerable contribution to the growth of some markets outside the USA. But the licensing of four US manufacturers, intended to ensure a maximum rate of development, resulted, by the mid-1960s, in intense competition and price cutting within the USA. This, in turn, was to have repercussions on prices in the rest of the world, reaching a peak during the early-1970s with the expiry of the ICI patents and the emergence of direct competition from the dominant US manufacturer, Abbott Laboratories. Desirable though such competition is from the viewpoint of existing users, it does tend to limit the funds that manufacturing companies are prepared to risk on further research, so important for the gibberellins because of the slowness with which practical applications can be identified. The existence of strong competition has certainly had an inhibiting effect on ICI's growth regulator research over the last few years.

With hindsight it can be seen that, if licences had not been granted to other manufacturers, the problem would have been minimised. Improvements in efficiency of GA manufacture have generally been difficult. Following the early improvements resulting from normal process development, subsequent increases in yield have depended largely on progressive mutation of the organism—a slow and more than usually difficult task in the case of *Gibberella fujikuroi*. Thus, without the original 'know-how' and the opportunity to make process improvements while protected by patents, late entrants into the field of manufacture would have been faced with very severe obstacles.

If gibberellic acid had been discovered some twenty years later, the emphasis of research and subsequent development might have taken a very different form, with a much stronger input from ICI. However, because of the unusually complex nature of the work, it must be concluded that the practical development of any new plant growth regulator is likely to require the same kind of collaboration between research workers in industry and agriculture that has characterised the history of the gibberellins.

The early work on gibberellins and their potential in agriculture has been comprehensively reviewed by Brian [2] and Wittwer and Bukovac [3]; a later account is given by Turner [4].

References

[1] Cross B E, Grove J F, McMillan J, Mulholland T P C (1956) 'Gibberellic acid Part IV. The structures of gibberic and allogibberic acids and possible structure for gibberellic acid' *Chemy Ind.* **36,** 954–55

[2] Brian P W (1959) 'Effects of gibberellins on plant growth and development' *Biol. Rev.* **34,** 37–84

[3] Wittwer S H, Bukovac M J (1958) 'The effects of gibberellin on economic crops' *Econ. Bot.* **12,** 213–55

[4] Turner J N (1972) 'Practical uses of gibberellins in agriculture and horticulture' *Outl. Agric.* **7** (1), 14–20

Chapter 8

Taking stock

Historically, the mid-point of this chronicle should be the year 1953, when Jealott's Hill celebrated its 25th anniversary, proudly, with marquees, distinguished visitors and tours of the laboratories and fields.

History, however, is dynamic; even as this book is being written the mid-point is changing. But there was, without doubt, a turning-point which at least began around this time; though 'point' is too exact a term for the somewhat protracted coming-of-age of the Station. This was to occupy some ten years, during which period Jealott's Hill changed from being the testing-ground for the products of research and commerce of Divisions geographically and organisationally remote, and emerged as a complete research establishment, capable of generating and following through its own chemical 'leads'.

Not only was the change protracted, it involved a catharsis and a 'baptism of fire' more literal than metaphoric.

In the mid-1950s, ICI's crop protection chemistry was carried out in the Midlands and in the North West of England, far removed from the biological and agricultural pursuits of Jealott's Hill. Chemists at Runcorn and at Blackley made every effort to relate their synthetic programmes to their colleagues' screening results, but there was a time-lag, opportunity for discussion was limited, and such geographical separation was seen as a constraint that could, and should, be removed. In 1954, W R Boon and his team of organic chemists from the crop protection section at Blackley, A Calderbank, R Ghosh, R F Homer and J A Silk—moved to Jealott's Hill where F L Sharp and C E Shepherd had already formed the nucleus of a formulation research section, and they were joined in 1956/7 by the first generation of organic chemists to be recruited direct to Jealott's Hill—R J W Cremlyn, A J Floyd and L A Summers. The new team joined forces with the Jealott's Hill biologists testing chemicals with potential outlets in agriculture and public health (many of whom have already appeared in this book); the microbiologists J L and Kay Charlton and J N Turner, investigating industrial spoilage problems; and S H Crowdy, D Rudd Jones and (later) K J Bent, who moved to Jealott's Hill from the Akers laboratory at Welwyn, to continue studies, already begun there, into systemic fungicidal activity.

Meanwhile, work continued in the sciences supportive to the crop production interests of the Company; R C Brian, G C Mees, D G Morgan and T E Tomlinson were among those whose researches in the fields of physical sciences, soils and plant physiology laid foundations for future projects at Jealott's Hill. But the balance of the Station was changing, and relations between the crop production side and the burgeoning team of 'protectionists' were not always of the easiest; Jealott's Hill, the purpose-built site headquarters, and Hawthorndale, the red-brick Victorian country house, were for a time worlds apart.

Barriers, however, cannot long survive in a climate of improvisation and make-do; and this, above all, characterised the Jealott's Hill of the mid-1950s, at least insofar as crop protection research was concerned.

The original buildings of Jealott's Hill and Hawthorndale were suddenly quite inadequate, and plans were drawn up for new laboratories, green-houses and offices.

Such expansion takes time; as an interim measure some most unpromis-ing temporary accommodation was pressed into service, including the old bull pens close to the farmyard. It is unlikely that there remains, unexploited, any further witticism on this theme. Another, purpose-built, shed of corrugated iron on timber framing, was even more temporary than intended, its demise accelerated by the unscheduled launch of an exploding autoclave containing one of Ghosh's more surprising reactions.

Synthetic Chemistry Laboratories 1958

New chemical laboratories were commissioned in 1957 and brought into operation in 1958. In time for the arrival of a second generation of chemists, the buildings initially provided accommodation for organic synthesis, biochemistry and formulation, and formed the core from which the present-day complex has developed. Botanists, entomologists and plant pathologists also shared in the building activity of the late 1950s; at the same time, they were reviewing their research processes, introducing greater realism into the design of screening tests, continuing the move away from *in vitro* towards *in vivo* methods, and helping to systematise the data-handling techniques used as the cornerstone of structure/activity correlation and analogue synthesis.

In 1958, the commercial facts of life made it urgently necessary for ICI to review, *in toto,* its involvement in the crop protection business 'so as to economise and make better and more selective use of resources' or, in other words, to turn what had become an unprofitable enterprise into a profitable one.

A year later, in February 1959, redundancies were announced which affected almost one-third of the technical and managerial staff of Plant Protection Ltd. The Company's London headquarters, Bolton House, was relinquished and Fernhurst became the business and administrative head-quarters; CAC was wound up. ICI and Plant Protection's undoubted loss was the gain of university, government and other organisations world-wide. But in the UK, where facile movement from job to job is less common than in many other countries, there was a sense of shock, and 'Black Friday' was to live in the collective consciousness of employees and uninvolved observers for many years. In the long run, it is doubtful if anyone suffered; and Plant Protection's loss of experienced men was made good by the recruitment, in the more buoyant situation of 1964, of a number of specialists rather suddenly 'available' as a result of the contraction of the UK Government's colonial responsibilities.

But, even before this, Jealott's Hill had gained J F H Cronshey and D Price Jones from Fernhurst and J M Winchester from Yalding.

So much for the catharsis. The fire followed soon after when, one night in March 1963, the chance juxtaposition of an electrical fault beneath the floor, a cylinder of acetylene gas above it, and a too-plentiful supply of inflammable solvents all around resulted in the total destruction of one wing of the 'new' chemical block and extensive damage to the rest of the building.

The fire, however, and the inquest into its causes, led swiftly and directly to a new professionalism. In the designing of subsequent buildings, potential fireways (for example in roof and underfloor) were blocked, additional smoke doors specified and installed, and metal was used in the construction of solvent cupboards and drying cabinets. Gas cylinders were racked outside the buildings, together with any sizeable quantities of inflammable solvents in overnight storage. Drawing on the experience of ICI's manufacturing Divisions and with with the help of A E Sarney as Fire Officer and R C Clinch as Safety Officer, a 'Code of Safe Practice' was drawn up and embodied in a staff training programme.

By modern standards the steps taken may appear elementary, but they were the beginnings of an awareness of both Company and individual responsibility whose justification is seen in Jealott's Hill's subsequent excellent safety record. Perhaps the least foreseen problem arose from insurance assessment. What is the fair and proper value to place on samples of novel chemical compounds, often the fruits of long and skilful synthetic processes? Should it be related to effort already invested or to the one in ten thousand chance for each sample that it might have proved a commercial 'winner'? The answer is debatable, but, after the fire, the chemical sample bank was relocated, and experimental records were duplicated in microfilm.

Lessons had been learned; now there was a great deal of inconvenience to put up with. Some of the chemists were 'evacuated' to laboratories in other ICI Divisions. Others found it impossible to complete research in hand, and the work of the whole Station was for a time drastically reduced.

But in the meantime, it was seen that, even had there been no fire, the laboratories would, again, have been inadequate. The phoenix which arose from the ashes a year later was a bigger and stronger bird; more suitable provision was made for work with organophosphorous derivatives, and the first stage of the Metabolism and Residues Section was established. The commitment of the 1950s was confirmed, and a base was established for a further, and greater, expansion that was to follow during the next ten years.

Outlook on Agriculture

In quieter vein, the second half of the 1950s saw the establishment of the ICI-sponsored and produced agricultural review journal *Outlook on Agriculture*. Launched in 1956 under the editorship of E J McNaughton, the first issue carried a personal message from the then Chairman of ICI, Sir Alexander Fleck, and a foreword by S W Cheveley.

An obvious candidate for 'the axe' when, in 1959, economies were sought, it miraculously survived; this was surely an act of faith; and possibly of hope; there could have been little charity to spare in an organisation faced with the unpalatable truth that it was losing money fast. *Outlook's* survival owed itself to the same corporate spirit that launched that other, much-loved ICI journal *Endeavour* at the tail-end of the depression of the late 1920s/early 1930s. Over the next twenty-two years *Outlook* was to maintain the standard set by McNaughton, under the Editorship successively of C C Tanner (1961–66), D Price Jones (1966–72), D J Halliday (1972–75) and F C Peacock. Its format changed little, its presentation remained somewhat conservative; but in content and distribution it was to become increasingly international in character.

Intelligence

Until 1954, when the Direction of Jealott's Hill and Hawthorndale began to be drawn together, the two Libraries were independent of one another. A technical intelligence service was provided by both; D J Halliday, Mary Peacock, Frances Atkins and others at Jealott's Hill catered for the Station's crop production interests while McNaughton, D Leatherdale and Joan Salter at Hawthorndale were building up a similar service on the crop protection side. Fernhurst Library also ran a technical index with a more commercial outlook. Samples of chemicals for testing had to be indexed and test results made available; but, with an annual intake at the time of no

1 25th Anniversary Luncheon,
    July 1953 Left to right:
    Rt Hon Sir Thomas Dugdale,
        Minister of Agriculture;
    Sir Alexander Fleck,
        Chairman, ICI;
    S W Cheveley,
        Chairman, CAC;
    John Rogers,
        retiring Chairman, ICI.

2 HRH, The Duke of Edinburgh's
    visit, April 1956.
    HRH Prince Philip and W R Boon

3 Left to right: W G Templeman,
    A H Lewis, HRH Prince Philip
    and A J Low

1

2

3

4

Bipyridylium herbicides

1 Paraquat residue analysis
2 Broad bean after leaf uptake of
   diquat; one leaf in darkness
3 Just after removal of black bag
4 The leaf after exposure to light
   for 20 minutes

more than 2000 compounds per year, one person—Joan Stanley—was able to look after these needs and, on occasion, to provide rudimentary structure/activity searches.

The crisis of 1959 resulted first in a cutback in library staff and facilities, then to amalgamation of the three Libraries under N Wright and finally, in 1965, and under the direction of J A Silk, to the building-up of an altogether more sophisticated Technical Information Section which came to encompass all the previous intelligence functions, and made extensive use of links to the computer facilities of Pharmaceuticals and Agricultural Divisions. ASSASSIN now covers reports, library material and patents, while CROSSBOW plus BCDF provide structure/activity correlation. KWIC indexes meet a variety of needs within the section and outside it, and microfilm plays an increasing role in management of the ever-growing volume of information.

This was one of a number of research support units which either owed their inception to, or were developed during this time of change. In the second category, the development of formulation technology was of major importance.

Formulation

Part art, part science and part technology, formulation is a crucial enabling step between discovery and practical application. On an intrinsically active chemical, formulation can confer persistence, rainfastness or mobility, favour specificity, reduce handling hazards or enhance convenience. Misunderstood or ignored, it can reduce the efficacy of a compound or cause it to fail to meet registration requirements. Formulation research, then, is a factor common to all the developments reviewed in this book; and it has been an important feature of work at Jealott's Hill for many years.

Agricultural chemicals—apart from seed dressing specialities—have always been formulated, by tradition, as dusts, wettable powders and emulsifiable concentrates. Handling or environmental disadvantages of the first two, and cost or phytotoxicity problems with the third, led workers at Jealott's Hill in 1959/60 to consider the possible use in agriculture of cream-like formulations in which, ideally, a high concentration of solid particles of very small size could be supported stably in water, with good thermal stability and dispersion properties. The first target for such formulations was the horticultural market, and products such as gamma-BHC, captan, dithianon and menazon were amongst the first to be investigated. J Rickards and L A Summers played a leading part in the early stages of this work in which Dyestuffs know-how and specialist milling technology provided a starting point; and satisfactory formulations containing up to 8 lb/gal solids were ultimately derived. A pair of 20-gallon bead mills was installed at Yalding, and, with the launching of 'Gammacol' in 1962, the day of the 'col' formulation had dawned. In some ways it proved a false dawn, since the servicing and control of this new process initially stretched the factory's technical resources to the limit; but from the needs of the moment grew a strengthened works experimental department, the nucleus of support activities vital to the future expansion at Yalding.

Physical Techniques

Belief in the possibility of the rational design of biologically active molecules led to the formation, during this intensely creative transitional period, of research groups studying structure/activity relationships (J A Farrington, R C Bridges) physical parameters (B G White) the effect of formulation on particle size and spray deposits (K J Heritage, D Seaman) and of chemicals on the surface and sub-cellular structure of plants (C E Price, C A Hart).

The use of high-speed and time-lapse photography in the hands of N Cattlin produced some remarkable pictures, one of which has been used as the cover design for this book.

It also led to an awareness of the educational and demonstrational value of photography, and to the subsequent creation of a display centre where the work of the station could be demonstrated by means of static displays, slide-tape presentations and films to an ever-increasing flow of visitors to Jealott's Hill.

The crisis had passed; and the second twenty-five years was to prove even more productive than the first.

Chapter 9

Bipyridylium herbicides

Gravity, steam power and penicillin, so the story goes, were all discovered by accident. To the continuing dismay of scientists who prefer to believe that discovery is the logical outcome of disciplined thinking the chance observation, followed by recognition of its value, is the more common recipe. It is, of course, important who makes the observation. Had Newton not been a physicist the apple which, legend has it, fell upon his head, might have occasioned, instead of the revelation of gravitational force, nothing more remarkable than an early description of codling moth.

ICI's herbicide synthetic effort in the early 1950s, following the successful assimilation into farming practice of the phenoxy acids, 2,4-D and MCPA, was directed towards the discovery of further compounds with a selective action. But in place of an apple, the 'little acorn' from which, as is well known, 'large oaks' are wont to grow had been lying dormant since 1947, when a field observation had recorded that the quaternary salt dodecyl-trimethyl ammonium bromide, used as a surfactant, was surprisingly phytotoxic.

In 1954, this chemical and a number of close relatives were re-tested and it was recognised that 'quaternaries', as a group, possessed herbicidal properties. A number of quaternary salts was then selected by R L Jones from the specimen collection at Dyestuffs Division and tested by J Stubbs and R C Brian at Jealott's Hill. For the most part, even at the 10 lb/acre rate regarded as the standard of interest for new leads, they were uninspiring; but there were two exceptions, and these two killed all the test plants at rates as low as 0·1 lb/acre. The 'acorn' had begun to grow.

The active chemicals were 2,2'- and 4,4'-bipyridylium quaternary ammonium salts. The 2,2'-bipyridylium, or N N'-ethylene-2,2'-bipyridylium dibromide, was the compound now known as diquat (**I**, page 68). The other was quickly supplanted, some six weeks later, when the closely related compound 1,1'-dimethyl-4,4'-bipyridylium dichloride, or paraquat (**II**), was synthesised and found to be even more active.

The properties of the new compounds were curious, but not at all what was wanted. They damaged green plant tissue rapidly but were adsorbed and rendered inactive almost instantaneously by soil, which ruled out the possibility of weed pre-emergence use. As foliar sprays, they were found to control a wide range of common annual weeds including several that had proved to be resistant to hormone weedkillers. However, with the vision of an improved MCPA as the yardstick by which to measure success, possible outlets for diquat were summarised, with little enthusiasm, in the words: 'a non-persistent weedkiller, with potential use on bulb farms and in market gardens, especially as high fertility weeds such as chickweed *(Stellaria media)* and annual nettle *(Urtica urens),* are very susceptible. In view of its activity on a wide range of weeds, including grasses, diquat might be of value in the treatment of clean fallow and possibly as a directed spray in cotton, maize, sugar cane and banana'. Neither selectivity nor soil application was a possible option with the bipyridyliums and their future was thought to be strictly limited.

I diquat (dibromide)

II paraquat (dichloride)

III morfamquat (dichloride)

It was not until the criteria of selectivity and action through soil were abandoned that the potential uses of diquat and paraquat became apparent. There is no doubt that the innovation represented by the bipyridyls, and by paraquat in particular, lay not so much in their biological properties but in the realisation of how these properties might be put to use. Much of the credit for this recognition must be ascribed to W R Boon who provided the drive and sheer persistence which were essential in overcoming prejudice and objection to the development of techniques which have since revolution-ised farming technology [1].

Such novel ideas cut across many of the established tenets of good husbandry and, in order to demonstrate that they were practicable, and that their adoption would be of benefit to the farmer, a development programme unique in the history of Jealott's Hill began to take shape.

But before recounting the course of this programme, and the effects the bipyridyls had upon the farming scene, it is necessary to describe some of the physical, biochemical and biological properties of the compounds, since it was only by virtue of their unique combination of instant action and rapid de-activation that their use in agriculture was possible.

The bipyridyl ring is common to all the highly active quaternary salts, and bipyridyls are all highly ionised salts which are very soluble in water.

Because their value as crop protection chemicals largely stems from their rapid adsorption to soil, intensive studies were carried out, by B A G Knight and T E Tomlinson at Jealott's Hill, on the mechanism of, and degree of, adsorption to many types of soil. (As early as 1955 Brian had shown that soils could adsorb and inactivate diquat in quantities up to 5% of the weight of soil). Adsorption to clays is particularly strong, while soil organic matter can also adsorb large quantities of the herbicide, although not so firmly. Up to a limiting concentration, defined as the strong adsorption capacity, a solution of diquat or paraquat in equilibrium with soil contains no detectable herbicide.

The capacity of various soils, from very sandy to clay, to adsorb paraquat, was calculated to range from about 50 to nearly 3000 lb ion/acre inch, and it was predicted that no problem would arise from the continued use of paraquat; this has been substantiated over a period of some sixteen years.

This capacity for inactivation by soil results from two important structural features common to both diquat and paraquat. First, they incorporate two positive charges per molecule; second, the molecules are flat or can assume a planar conformation. The former facilitates adsorption on to negatively charged surfaces while the latter enables diquat and paraquat to penetrate the expanding lattice layers in the clay minerals of the soil. Association is thus very close, and herbicide adsorbed in this way is extremely difficult to replace by other cations. Most important, the herbicide is inactivated and unavailable for uptake by plant roots.

Soon after the initial discoveries it was found that quaternaries based on 2,2'- as well as those based on 4,4'-bipyridyls were capable of being converted by strong reducing agents such as zinc to highly coloured radicals. Those from diquat were bright green and those from paraquat, blue. Following the synthesis, by R F Homer, and screening of a large number of bipyridylium quaternary salts, it was observed that only those that could be reduced in this way were herbicidally active. This formation of radicals is now known to be fundamental to the action of diquat and paraquat on plants and their colour is also the basis of sensitive methods developed at Jealott's Hill for detecting and analysing diquat and paraquat.

Simplistically, ease of reduction of the compounds may be regarded as a function of their stereochemistry; in particular, their ability to assume a planar conformation. 2,3'- and 3,3'-quaternaries were not reduced, nor were they active. These studies linked activity with radical production and a working hypothesis for their mode of action was put forward [2].

It was suggested that bipyridylium quaternary herbicides were not active per se but that activation by the plant must first take place. Such activation requires a reduction to radicals by the normal photosynthetic and respiratory activities of the plant. Supporting this suggestion, it was shown that treated plants in the light were damaged rapidly whereas plants in the dark remained virtually unharmed for several days. Plants containing no chlorophyll (e.g. wheat, germinated in darkness) were similarly unaffected by diquat.

However, radical production in the plant was not the only requirement for rapid activity. G C Mees found that oxygen was essential, since plant tissue in an oxygen-free atmosphere was not damaged by diquat [3] and this observation led to the suggestion that radicals were oxidised to hydrogen peroxide within plant tissue. Hydrogen peroxide production in plants treated with diquat and paraquat was proved and, as this was known to be phytotoxic, it appeared that hydrogen peroxide might be the true herbicide. But the presence of peroxide in treated plants was no proof of its direct participation in diquat or paraquat action, and superoxide O_2^- also present in plants following applications of diquat and paraquat, was suggested by J A Farrington as another possible phytotoxic agent. It is now generally accepted that hydrogen peroxide and/or superoxide are phytotoxic agents produced by oxidation of diquat and paraquat radicals giving rise to the well-known desiccation symptoms associated with these herbicides, but a further possibility explored at Jealott's Hill postulated the destruction of chlorophyll by radicals. Careful observation of plants treated with bipyridylium herbicides indicates that both activities, i.e. desiccation and chlorophyll destruction occur side by side in damaged plants.

Uptake and Movement in Plants

In retrospect, it is surprising how much was learned about the uptake and translocation of diquat within a matter of months after its discovery, using improvised techniques because radio-labelled chemicals and sensitive methods of analysis were not then available. For example, R C Brian studied the uptake of the chemical by eluting diquat from treated leaves after various periods of time. Sodium hydroxide added to the eluate resulted in the formation of a red colouration which indicated the presence of unabsorbed diquat. Brian's early studies of the movement of bipyridyls employed broad beans, since it was found that diquat and paraquat damaged the cells of the bean plant releasing phenolic compounds which were rapidly oxidised to red pigments and these were easily visible. Such unsophisticated experiments at Jealott's Hill soon established that uptake was a rapid process (a phytotoxic dose of a bipyridylium herbicide is taken up in minutes; hence rain falling soon after treatment has little effect on activity) and even in 1955 it was known that diquat and paraquat moved mainly in the xylem of plants. It was also found at this time that diquat entered plants via the roots as well as by the leaves, but not when application was by way of a soil drench; thus the ability of soil to inactivate diquat was also established.

The supposition that diquat moved mainly in the xylem of plants has since been confirmed for both diquat and paraquat using radio-labelled chemicals and more sophisticated methods of analysis. Thus, translocation is mainly upward and recent experiments have shown that the amount of movement correlates with rates of transpiration. Hence the early symptoms of damage, particularly on grasses within 1–3 days of treatment, are those of desiccation confined to the upper regions of the plant. If this were the entire story diquat and paraquat would be contact herbicides only, with little effect either on the lower regions of plants or on regrowth. However, some downward movement occurs and although the amounts may be small paraquat, in particular, affects unsprayed parts of plants and inhibits subsequent regrowth.

The downward movement is known as 'reverse xylem flow' and it results as a secondary effect of damage to the distal portion of the leaf where the herbicide accumulates. Reverse xylem flow is very important to bipyridylium action since this mechanism enables diquat and paraquat to be translocated to meristematic regions of the plant giving longer term control of plant growth than would be possible from contact action only. Therefore, factors which encourage reverse flow have an important influence on herbicide efficiency. Downward movement is greatly increased when the air is humid at the time of treatment and when the soil is dry or at a low temperature.

In summary, then, the conditions most conducive to effective treatment with bipyridyls are those of high atmospheric humidity and where the soil is dry and cold (though undesirable residues in crops such as potatoes may also be increased in these situations). Low light intensity or total darkness also leads to increased efficiency. Thus the adage that 'the early bird catches the worm' is not true of those who use bipyridylium quaternaries as herbicides, since evening sprays most nearly approximate to the conditions of humidity and darkness ideal for efficient uptake, movement and subsequent activity of diquat and paraquat.

Agricultural Uses of Diquat

Development followed closely on the heels of discovery and the first problem was that of deciding where, initially, effort should be concentrated. The characteristics of the new, quick acting, non-persistent herbicide diquat, suggested that it could be employed for selective weed control in cereals, control of weeds immediately before crop emergence, pre-harvest desiccation of crops such as, in the UK, potatoes and clovers and perhaps control of woody weeds.

Diquat as a Selective Herbicide

The experimental expertise acquired during the selective herbicide campaign of the 1940s no doubt influenced the choice of weed control in cereal crops as a major 'target' in the development of diquat.

It had been shown that diquat could control broad-leaved annual weeds very effectively and that damage to grasses was only temporary. On the basis of observations at Jealott's Hill in greenhouse tests and on one-yard-square experimental plots it was conceded that some initial scorch of cereals might occur, and with this reservation a team from Plant Protection Limited at Fernhurst embarked, in 1957, on a programme of field tests involving treated areas usually of two hectares. It was soon apparent that the British farmer was less than enthusiastic about having his young wheat, barley and oats heavily scorched even in the interests of scientific endeavour—not indeed surprising, since ICI had only recently taught him that phenoxyacetic herbicides would control weeds in his cereals with no deleterious effect on the crop. Even the most co-operative and progressive farmer was reluctant to permit the spraying of additional trial plots for later growth stage comparisons when he saw the damage done to earlier sprayed plots. The scorch, in fact, was transitory; wheat yields were reduced by 5 to 10%, oats not at all. But barley was more sensitive and damage was usually unacceptable. The project was duly abandoned and interest in diquat was focused on non-crop situations and pre-harvest crop desiccation.

On reflection, it is a constant source of wonderment that so many farmers are willing to co-operate in the field testing of new ideas. The association between experimenter and co-operator is one of mutual respect and is motivated by true scientific curiosity; and this is as good a place as any to state that it is highly valued and appreciated by organisations such as ICI.

Diquat Development in the USA

At this point it was decided to look further afield and, in particular, to the United States of America, where herbicide use had developed to a much greater extent for both agricultural and non-agricultural applications and where ICI's agent, Chipman Chemical Co. Inc. occupied an important place in the industrial herbicide market.

As a consequence, in 1958, a three-man team from Fernhurst, H P Allen, T C Breese and A F J Wheeler, spent several months in the USA endeavouring to find commercial uses for diquat; particular attention was paid to the possibilities of industrial weed control outlets such as railroads and power lines, the defoliation of fire-breaks (also examined in Australia) summer fallow and pre-harvest crop desiccation. There was considerable interest in the compound but it became clear that, whilst there was a big future for diquat as a pre-harvest desiccant for potatoes, lucerne and clovers, and in the limited area of storm-proof, closed-boll cotton (the defoliation of open-boll cotton required further refinement) it was not acceptable for general control of vegetation. Perversely, where diquat had been too phytotoxic to use on young cereals as a selective herbicide, it was not active enough as a general herbicide because its effect upon grasses, and especially perennial grasses, was too transitory.

Potato Haulm Desiccation

Meanwhile, at Jealott's Hill, one of the largest and most successful developments of diquat was gathering momentum. This account of the use of diquat to aid the harvesting of potatoes, illustrates well the kind of problem which may, and often does, arise between the introduction of a new technique and its eventual adoption into farming practice.

Diquat had been discovered at a time when increasingly sophisticated

1 Harvesting sunflower after
  desiccation with diquat
2 Weed control in 4-year old
  rubber with paraquat
3 Weed control in bananas with
  paraquat

1

Pasture renovation and direct
   drilling

1 Spraying grassland with
    paraquat
2 Early work on pasture
    renovation
3 Massey-Ferguson drill modified
    for direct drilling

2

3

Bipyridyls: weed control

1 Aquatic weed control
2 Spraying weeds before
  planting rice
3 Weed control in tea
  with 'Gramoxone'

1 Biology Laboratories and
  Glasshouses at dusk
2 Herbicide screening test
3 Herbicide sprayer

mechanised equipment called for the use of chemical desiccants to facilitate harvesting. Potatoes, the most important crop requiring such treatment in the UK, were commonly sprayed with products such as sulphuric acid, sodium chlorate and sodium arsenite. These materials were unpleasant and hazardous to handle; sodium arsenite, in fact, was shortly to disappear from the market because of its highly toxic nature. The time was right for the introduction of a new product with none of these disadvantages. Initial field tests with diquat on potatoes in 1955–1958, followed by development trials in 1959 and 1960, proved the efficacy and superiority of the new compound over existing products, and diquat was introduced commercially for potato haulm desiccation in 1961.

The proposed use of diquat on potatoes necessitated a variety of tests to prove the absence of deleterious effects, e.g. to establish that the sprayed haulm was not palatable to cattle (as was that treated with sodium arsenite), that residue levels in tubers were very low and safe for human consumption, that tuber skins matured normally, seed stored and sprouted satisfactorily and that there was no taint in the produce when cooked.

No doubts were raised by any of these tests; but, in 1959, the condition known as 'stem-end rot' was noticed by G Douglas in tubers from two of the many trials conducted in the UK during that year.

Stem-end rot is a small zone of necrotic tissue which appears at the basal (stem) end of the tuber where it originally joined the stolon of the plant. Its appearance, though infrequent, is specifically related to the use of chemical desiccants; it had previously been recorded as resulting from sodium arsenite treatments and was subsequently reported for other desiccants such as sodium chlorate and dinoseb [4]. The rot, initially caused by a high local concentration of chemical, may extend by secondary pathogen infection and cause storage losses. Even though, at worst, only one-fifth of one per cent of the diquat-sprayed acreage was ever affected, the use of this otherwise excellent product was bound to be constrained unless an answer to the problem could be found. In the event, its resolution was to take eight years; the eventual successful outcome was very largely the result of studies by D W R Headford.

When the problem arose with diquat in the UK during 1959, a feature of the year had been the abnormally dry summer, and the subsequent incidence of stem-end rot during commercial usage in the early 1960s occurred mainly in the dry seasons of 1961 and 1964. However, J Stubbs' field trials in India in 1960, carried out under drought conditions, had failed to produce stem-end rot, and pot tests under glasshouse conditions at Jealott's Hill also failed to demonstrate tuber damage, even at severe moisture stress levels. It was clear that drought alone could not be responsible, and attention turned to other environmental variables known to influence the uptake and movement of diquat within plants. The turning-point came, following the demonstration by R C Brian of the marked effect of humidity on the uptake of bipyridyl herbicides [5], when Headford showed, in a pot test in which potatoes were drought stressed to the point of incipient wilt and sprayed with diquat in an atmosphere of 80% relative humidity, that the concentration of diquat recorded in the tubers was ten times normal; and a significant proportion of the tubers developed stem-end rot. The physiological mechanism has been discussed earlier in this chapter. Further tests confirmed that only this particular combination of weather factors resulted in damage. A very detailed survey of all the known commercial cases was then carried out and, in particular, with the help of A J Low, a mass of meteorological data was examined. Although high air humidity was clearly a feature of these incidents, it was considered impractical to base recommendations on this factor since it is subject to such short-term fluctuations. Instead, attention was focused on the records of rainfall and soil moisture and a warning system based on these data was devised. It involved the Company's regional offices in receiving, weekly during the spraying season (May–October), data on soil moisture deficits and rainfall from 58 meteorological stations covering the main potato growing areas. During prolonged dry weather farmers were recommended to consult their local office and were advised not to spray if the soil moisture deficit was greater than 3 inches and less than 0·5 inch of rain had fallen in the previous five days. The scheme was introduced in the UK in 1968 and has operated successfully ever since.

Pre-harvest Desiccation of Oilseed Crops

Improved varieties, better use of irrigation and fertilizers resulted in striking increases in the 1960s and '70s in the world acreage of oilseed crops, which were producing, by 1973, 28·3 million tonnes of vegetable oil per annum. A major constraint to further increase was the difficulty of harvesting the crop in good condition. Seeds mature prior to full senescence of the rest of the plant, and weeds and green crop material impede the working of the combine harvesters, particularly in a wet season. Trash is picked up with the seed, increasing its moisture content. Delay in harvesting results in seed loss due to shattering of the pods and to bird damage. The answer was found in desiccating the standing crop and weeds chemically as soon as the seed had matured, when harvesting could be carried out earlier, quicker, and more efficiently.

The use of chemical desiccants is now well-established, but materials available until comparatively recently—phosphates, chlorates, DNOC, dinoseb and sulphuric acid—had disadvantages such as slow action, toxicity, persistent residues and corrosive properties. Diquat, introduced for this purpose in the mid-1960s, has a rapid effect on all green plant parts, and an action unaffected by rainfall and largely independent of variations in climate. Residues in plant parts are extremely low, and harmless to animals, and because diquat is insoluble in lipoids, there are no residues in the oil from the crop. It is safe and convenient to apply.

In comprehensive trials in Poland on sunflower, diquat, sprayed from the air at 0·4 kg/ha in 50–80 litres of water, advanced the harvesting date by sixteen days, almost halved the time of the harvesting operation, and reduced the moisture content of the seed from 25% to 12%.

On rape in Czechoslovakia aerial application of diquat at 0·5 to 0·6 kg/ha in 70–100 litres water increased seed yield by 20%.

Similar advantages of diquat pre-harvest desiccation have been demonstrated on crops of linseed, castor bean, cotton, poppy, radish, safflower, sesame and soya.

Aquatic Weed Control

Early work by W G L Austin at Jealott's Hill established that concentrations in the water of 0·25–1·0 ppm of diquat or paraquat rapidly killed submerged or floating weed growth, while surface sprays were effective against emergent growth near to the bank. The herbicides were rapidly absorbed into the vegetation, residues in the water declined rapidly and the water was safe to use for channel irrigation of crops within 48 hours. The environmental impact of chemicals introduced into natural waters is clearly of great importance; at herbicidal concentrations in the water, paraquat and diquat have a wide safety margin to fish. It soon became evident, however, that the indirect results of weed destruction, in habitat destruction and in changes in dissolved oxygen concentration in the water, were of greater importance than any possible direct effects. Such indirect consequences were investigated in the newly-formed Ecology Section, and field trials were monitored in a wide range of aquatic sites. These trials were supported by laboratory studies, and included collaborative work with ICI's Brixham laboratory and with the Nature Conservancy and other independent laboratories. Conditions of use were established to avoid undesirable indirect effects on the aquatic environment which, together with extensive work in the USA, has resulted in wide use of the bipyridylium herbicides in aquatic weed control in many different countries.

The Introduction of Paraquat

Though development work in the UK and USA during the late 1950s had identified several uses for diquat, its limitations for grass weed control had become evident. But the Fernhurst team in the USA returned with the clear message that a herbicide with the attributes of diquat plus the ability to control grasses would have a considerable future. The amalgamation of Jealott's Hill and Fernhurst research capabilities at Jealott's Hill in 1959 provided the experience and manpower needed for the development of the related bipyridyl paraquat, which rapidly killed grasses as well as broadleaved plants.

Two opportunities for field testing paraquat in 1959 were taken. In the UK a programme of total weed control trials was initiated on behalf of Chipman Chemical Co. and, through ICI Malaya (now ICI Malaysia), the possibility of weed control in rubber was explored.

Industrial Uses

The industrial weed control market requires both rapid knock-down of vegetation and persistence of effect. A F J Wheeler's trials in the UK demonstrated not only the spectacularly rapid effect of paraquat alone on all green tissue, including grasses, but also showed that, when applied in admixture with residual herbicides such as diuron and simazine, a long-lasting effect, better than the additive effect of the individual components of the mixture, was obtained. These field results were positive and unmistakable, and wide patent cover was obtained for the invention. Recommendations for the industrial use of mixtures were made but, in addition, the possibilities of developing uses for paraquat (alone or in admixture) in orchards and plantations were recognised.

Weed Control in Rubber

Control of weeds in rubber plantations in Malaya (now Malaysia) in 1959 made extensive use of sodium arsenite, which was both cheap and effective. However, sodium arsenite was disliked both by Government and the estates because of its highly poisonous nature and its consequent risk to cattle. Jealott's Hill, via ICI Malaya, was asked whether alternative chemicals were available for this market; diquat and paraquat were among the chemicals selected for testing and a series of trials was conducted during May–September 1959 by R S L Jeater.

The main weeds at this time on the large estates were aggressive stoloniferous grasses such as buffalo grass *(Paspalum conjugatum)* and *Panicum nodosum,* both of which were controlled by sodium arsenite, although in young replanted rubber three or four rounds of spraying were required each year; in mature rubber with a closed canopy one round per year was usually sufficient.

In replicated trials on estates throughout Malaya it was quickly seen that, of the chemicals being evaluated, the bipyridyls were the most promising. Both diquat and paraquat gave a very rapid initial desiccation of the grass weeds. However, when diquat was used the stolons were only slightly affected and regrowth started within a week or ten days of application, in the high light intensity conditions found in young rubber plantations. With paraquat, after the initial rapid desiccation, a more persistent kill of the stolons was achieved, and a single application gave up to twelve weeks' satisfactory weed control.

In the shade of mature rubber trees, both chemicals gave extended weed control but, again, paraquat was more effective than diquat. These early trials also showed that diquat and paraquat were more rainfast than sodium arsenite; rain within an hour of spraying did not reduce the efficiency of the chemicals. Moreover, unlike sodium arsenite, they could be sprayed on to the bark of young rubber trees without causing damage.

The rhizomatous grass *Imperata cylindrica* was frequently seen as a weed problem on smallholder estates, and constituted a major problem because smallholders could not obtain a licence to use sodium arsenite. Paraquat controlled this weed more effectively than did diquat but control necessitated four applications at 10 to 14 day intervals. Another weed not controlled by a single application of paraquat was *Paspalum conjugatum.* The initial action of paraquat on this weed was extremely rapid under the high light intensities common in young rubber, blackening of the leaf occurring within an hour or two of treatment; unfortunately, this very rapid action inhibited the movement of paraquat in the plant and regrowth appeared within two weeks. Again, split applications of paraquat with a 10 to 14 day interval between the two proved to be effective.

A method for improving paraquat action on these difficult-to-control weeds by the use of chemicals which reduce the rate of photosynthesis is described later in this chapter.

Following these promising results further replicated trials were carried out in rubber in 1960. This second series fully confirmed the 1959 results on a range of grass species, and the work was extended to take in some of the more difficult broad-leaved weeds such as *Eupatorium odoratum* and *Melastoma malabathricum*. As before, some regrowth was noted after the first treatment, but a split application gave satisfactory control.

Up to this point trials work had made use of an efficient sprayer specially designed for field experiments. The final development, in 1961, concentrated on the application of paraquat by estate labour using the main types of knapsack sprayer then available in Malaya. These development trials proved that, even under such conditions, the compound gave satisfactory control of weeds on Malayan rubber estates. At the same time the work was extended into oil palm, the other major estate crop in Malaya. The problem here was to keep the harvesting paths and the 'drop circles' clear of weeds. In general, the weed flora on such estates was similar to that on the rubber estates but it included a number of ferns such as *Nephrolepis*, *Lygodium* and *Blechnum*. As in the earlier trials paraquat gave a very rapid knock-down of vegetation and continued to give a satisfactory suppression of weeds for a period of 8 to 12 weeks, depending on conditions.

During this development phase it was found that, in general, paraquat was less damaging than was sodium arsenite to the leguminous cover crops *Pueraria* and *Centrosema* growing between the rows of young rubber trees. Moreover, old oil palms could be destroyed rapidly to make way for young tree replacements by a basal injection of paraquat.

By the end of 1961, it was possible to formulate recommendations for the use of paraquat as a herbicide in Malayan plantations [6]. It was first marketed early in 1962 as PP910 and later as 'Gramoxone' when this name became the world-wide trade name used by ICI for herbicidal formulations containing paraquat.

Minimal Cultivations and Direct Drilling

By 1960, the physical properties of diquat and paraquat had been well defined and the importance of their unique behaviour in soil was recognised. Paraquat, like diquat, was rapidly and strongly adsorbed to soils and, once adsorbed, it was not available for uptake into plants through plant roots. Since it was also rapidly taken up through foliage, and plant death followed within days of spraying, paraquat was an ideal candidate for a technological development in crop production now popularly known as 'direct drilling' which, although not entirely new, had not thus far been employed in conjunction with a non-residual herbicide.

Direct drilling involved the sowing of crops into sward or stubble without prior cultivation; with a knowledge of the favourable properties of paraquat, it now became possible to conceive of drilling crop seeds into vegetation killed off with paraquat, though the realisation of this idea was to present many problems.

Pasture Renovation

Millions of acres of unproductive hill and lowland pastures in Britain are capable of improvement, but large tracts are beyond the scope of conventional agricultural implements due to unfavourable topography, stony soils or low-lying water-logged conditions.

Improvement of the more accessible pastures by burning, discing and re-seeding was practised in the 1920s and the term 'renovation' came into use. Pasture renovation is the improvement of any type of unproductive pasture; but, in terms of agricultural chemicals, it is thought of in connection with the improvement of non-ploughable land. In such a context it is important that existing vegetation is killed and a favourable rooting medium provided for the establishment of new species.

The discovery of new herbicides capable of killing grass species encouraged research workers at many Institutes to turn their attention to the substitution of chemicals for tillage. By the end of 1959 it was evident that paraquat was a particularly suitable chemical for use in pasture renovation.

Hill grazings and marginal land were the first situations to receive attention. The area of good permanent grass in the UK is small in relation to the stock-carrying capacity of the hill pasture and this limits the supply of winter feed for the breeding stock. Improvement of the hills would alleviate this position. The first experiments were carried out in mid-Wales by G Douglas, C J Lewis and H C McIlvenny [7] and they studied the effect of diquat and paraquat on the botanical composition of hill swards. The initial foliar scorch following spraying was similar with both herbicides, but many grass species were able to recover from the effect of diquat; it was soon shown that paraquat offered a greater potential for sward killing.

Grass species responded differently to low doses of the bipyridyls and there was some speculation that they might be used selectively to swing the balance of the hill sward in favour of the more nutritious fescue species. This approach, however, was abandoned as plant response was too critically conditioned by dose and stage of plant growth.

Studies then concentrated on paraquat for complete sward destruction prior to reseeding. Work on small plots, in which grass and clover seed was raked into the dead litter by hand, progressed to experimental areas of three acres and the use of farm implements. Encouragement came when lambs placed on re-seeded areas showed an increase in liveweight 40% greater than that of lambs on the hill, after 5 weeks of grazing.

Dead litter remaining after spraying still required some cultivation to open up the root mat and expose the underlying rooting medium for the new seeds. In some cases sheep were successfully walked over treated areas to tread the seeds into the surface litter.

At the same time work commenced in the lowlands. The agricultural value of lowland pastures is, in general, reflected by the component species of swards. Even in the best permanent pastures there is a small percentage of inferior species such as *Agrostis*. A pasture in which *Agrostis* is dominant is therefore less valuable than a ryegrass pasture, and upgrading or renovating may be worthwhile.

Low-lying flood meadows, where conventional methods of re-seeding were impracticable, were also investigated, with a similar success to that of the hill renovation programme, but treatment of the dead surface litter still proved a constraint to 'turning old pastures into new'. Close grazing or cutting the sward before spraying reduced the problem, but where litter was excessive or organic breakdown was low, cultivations were still required.

Direct Drilling of Cereals and Kale

After the work on grassland renovation was under way attention was directed to arable crops. The first experiment involving the new technique, described variously as 'sod seeding' or 'chemical ploughing' was laid down by A E M Hood, H R Jameson and R Cotterell at Jealott's Hill in the autumn of 1961, with winter wheat following eighty-year-old permanent pasture [8]. This experiment, which was destined to last for seven years, compared three major treatments:
(1) ploughing and cultivating;
(2) spraying the old sward with paraquat, followed by ploughing and cultivating;
(3) spraying the old sward with paraquat, with no following cultivation.

Winter wheat was sown conventionally in treatments 1 and 2 and, in treatment 3, it was drilled direct into the sprayed sward with a JEC 'Grasslands' Sod Seeder, the only machine available at the time whose coulters would penetrate undisturbed soil. Three nitrogen levels were superimposed on these treatments. Despite the very rough seed bed created by the Suffolk-type coulters used on this drill, yields from 'direct drilling' were extremely encouraging, reaching 2·9 tons grain/acre (7·25 tonnes/ha), which was not exceeded by conventional ploughing and cultivating.

Other trials followed in which wheat, barley and kale were successfully grown after grassland or stubbles using the new technique and a Massey-Ferguson combine drill which Hood modified by having heavy weights attached to bars fitted to each disc coulter to aid penetration of the soil. It was soon seen that problems could arise on heavy, poorly drained land and on fields where couch grass *(Agropyron repens)* was present; occasionally slugs had to be controlled. Generally, however, results were sufficiently promising to warrant more extensive investigation on a national basis. Benefits which were seen immediately included earlier sowing of barley in the spring on sprayed, undisturbed soil, and the firmer surface provided for strip-grazing cattle on direct-drilled kale, compared with that on cultivated land.

In August 1962 the launching of paraquat on the Plant Protection UK sales range as 'Gramoxone' initiated a considerable expansion in experimental and development work on what now came to be known as 'direct drilling'. Jealott's Hill field research was intensified by the creation of a new trials unit, under R S L Jeater, which, from 1963 until 1969, concentrated almost exclusively on examining various aspects of direct-drilled cereals. Field studies included the rate and time of application of paraquat, effect of nitrogen, influence of direct drilling on seed rate requirement and broadcasting versus combine drilling of fertilizer in a direct-drilling situation. Experiments were extended to outside farms.

Concurrently UK Development Department (UKDD) under H P Allen (then part of the Research and Development Department and based at Jealott's Hill) initiated farm-scale development work throughout the country in 1963. They started by persuading farmers to drill with their own conventional corn drills into sward and stubble, sprayed with paraquat but without any cultivation, and the variable results from direct drilling with such machines drew attention to the need for specially designed drills.

The first prototype, fitted with a knife-and-disc coulter on a Massey-Ferguson frame, was used extensively by Jealott's Hill Field Experiment Section and UKDD in 1964 and 1965; NAAS Experimental Husbandry Farms were loaned similar drills for their experiments during that period. In 1966 and afterwards the knife-and-disc was superseded by the triple-disc coulter, in wide use today in Bettinson drills in the UK and in other drills overseas.

The period 1963 to 1968 was one of varying fortunes for the direct drilling of cereals. It was clear that the idea had much to offer and that the triple-disc was a great improvement on the earlier coulter. It was equally clear that success for direct drilling winter wheat was far from predictable, especially on heavier soils. Gradually the technique was refined and guidelines were improved, but the behaviour of the 'below ground' parts of the cereal plant under direct drilling was still not well understood. The work of J R Finney, B A G Knight and D Riley at Jealott's Hill in 1968–9, which involved comparative studies on root performance of wheat, as influenced by soil physical properties in undisturbed and cultivated soils, did much to illuminate this subject, and heralded a considerable widening of interest by soil scientists throughout the UK in soil/direct drilling relationships.

The development of this technique became a commercial venture in the UK in the latter part of the 1960s, by which time the direct drilling of kale had become firmly established as a farm technique, and that of winter cereals was also beginning to advance [9], [10]. The Overseas Development Department, formed in 1964 as part of the Jealott's Hill R & D organisation based on Fernhurst, spearheaded a world-wide development programme with paraquat. This led to the direct drilling technique being studied in Australia and New Zealand and, through Plant Protection Ltd's distributors Chevron Chemical Co. in the USA, a part of the story which is told in a later chapter.

The establishment of a husbandry based on tillage and pulverisation of the soil, and developed over a period of more than two thousand years, is unlikely to be disrupted overnight, though the past seventy years have seen a growing awareness that such treatment is often detrimental to soil structure and useful mainly in the context of weed control. Thus the early excited prophecy, that direct drilling would relegate the plough to the status of a museum exhibit, is far from fulfilment. Nevertheless, world-wide, several million hectares a year are now drilled with the aid of paraquat.

A comprehensive review of work with the bipyridylium herbicides up to the late 1960s has been given by Calderbank [11].

4

Direct drilling

1 Bettinson 3-D drill
2 Moore Uni-drill
3 WMF-Howard 'Rotaseeder'
4 Gibbs Mk II direct drill

1

2

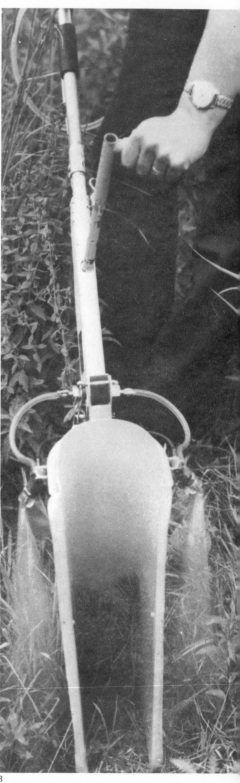

Bipyridyl application

1 A 'Vibrajet' clamped to the
  boom of a conventional sprayer,
  to adapt it for no-drift spraying
2 Inter-row weeding with the
  'Xpando'
3 'Arbogard' Mk II in use
  spraying 'Gramoxone' round
  young tree

Enhancement of Paraquat Activity

As experience was gained in the use of paraquat in direct drilling for crop production and for general weed control in a variety of situations, it became clear that certain deep-rooted perennial grasses and weeds were not adequately controlled and some annual species were resistant. These problem weeds desiccated satisfactorily within days of treatment, but because of their high potential for regrowth they were able to recover. It was obvious that ways of enhancing the herbicidal effect of paraquat should be sought.

It was shown earlier that treatment in the appropriate environment was all-important. Dull, humid days and dry soil are excellent conditions in which to spray paraquat and the evening is also favourable since humidity normally increases and decreasing light intensity is followed by a period of darkness. Dry and bright sunny days produce a quicker action, but the end effect will almost certainly be poorer control than that resulting from sprays in dull, humid conditions.

Ideally, the farmer would like both rapid desiccation and long-term control of the unwanted vegetation, but trials on specific major perennial weed targets such as couch grass in UK cereal stubbles and buffalo grass in Malaysian rubber plantations had shown that paraquat alone would not provide sufficiently long-term control of such weeds.

The case for considering mixtures of paraquat with soil-residual herbicides or foliar-translocated herbicides to achieve the double benefit of quick initial knockdown and persistent weed control was becoming apparent. Highly persistent soil-acting compounds such as the urea and triazine herbicides were already being used for industrial weed control. Wheeler's trials on mixed weed populations in the UK during 1959–1961 had demonstrated the advantage of combinations of paraquat with monuron, diuron, simazine and atrazine in terms of kill of existing vegetation plus long term weed control. Moreover, there was an unexpected bonus; not only did the residual component of the mixture prevent new weed seedlings from emerging, but a synergistic effect was apparent, that is, a greater-than-additive effect resulted from such combinations on the original weeds present at the time of spraying.

During the early 1960s considerable effort, both in the glasshouse and the field, was devoted to testing a large number of possible synergists for paraquat. These included known herbicides and a wide range of non-phytotoxic compounds which, at least on theoretical grounds, might be expected to potentiate paraquat. In all, over 500 candidates were examined, of which the most consistently synergistic with paraquat were compounds known to be photosynthetic inhibitors. The urea and triazine herbicides were the most potent examples of compounds of this nature.

The synergism derived from such admixtures with paraquat could be explained, at least partially, on the basis of interference with the Hill reaction of photosynthesis, a process which has already been seen to be responsible for the activation of paraquat within plants. Laboratory mode-of-action studies wtih diquat had shown that monuron, like darkness, inhibited the normal rapid desiccation of green plant tissue. Later, tests on whole plants showed this inhibition to be only temporary; slower initial desiccation was followed by improved suppression of regrowth. It was postulated that this postponement of scorching enabled more paraquat to penetrate into leaves before cellular damage limited further uptake, and this is now known to be true.

The most promising photosynthetic inhibitors to emerge from the screening programme, fenuron and bromacil, were tested by Headford on *Paspalum conjugatum* in rubber plantations in Malaysia in the autumn of 1964. At that time a particular need for better control of *Paspalum* had arisen as a result of the use of paraquat alone, which, by killing annual weeds, had encouraged spread of the perennial grass. Both herbicides proved to be markedly synergistic in combination with paraquat; when used as additives at doses low enough in themselves to be almost innocuous, the duration of weed control was increased four-fold over that achieved with paraquat alone. Such mixtures were not immediately developed in view of prevailing high chemical costs and the technical superiority of an alternative treatment discovered during the same trials programme. Complete eradication of *Paspalum* was effected by means of an initial sub-lethal dose of the systemic herbicide amitrole, followed within 1–2 weeks by paraquat. A tank-mix of these two herbicides was antagonistic (due, as with mixtures of paraquat and most slow-acting foliar herbicides, to rapid desiccation preventing uptake of the second component) but the sequential treatment was highly effective and was standard practice for some years.

Towards the end of the 1960s, however, increasing labour costs made this dual-application method of weed control less attractive. Diuron had been found to be as effective an additive as bromacil in the humid tropics, and the increased availability and lower price of this chemical led to its current use with paraquat for perennial weed control in rubber and oil plantations in the Far East. A similar mixture was developed for use in situations such as orchards in Europe, and coffee, sugar cane and bananas in South America. Combinations of paraquat with alternative herbicides of this type have since been developed for other plantation crops as, for example, mixtures with sima-zine for vines in Europe and with terbacil for citrus in Mediterranean areas.

Mixtures with selective residual herbicides were developed for pre-emergence application in arable crops, such as those with monolinuron for potatoes and those with linuron, alachlor or metribuzin for use prior to direct drilling soya beans in the Americas. The production of compatible formulations of paraquat with residual herbicides posed particular problems when physical studies first commenced in 1962. The cationic nature of paraquat precluded the use of many dispersing agents to maintain the relatively insoluble urea or triazine herbicides in satisfactory suspension in concentrated aqueous solutions. However, using the expertise in col formulation technology available at Jealott's Hill, suitable dispersing agents were developed. The first herbicide col, 'Gramonol' (paraquat plus monolinuron) was introduced onto the market in 1968 and was followed by 'Paracol' and 'Totacol' (paraquat plus diuron) in 1972 and 1974 respectively and 'Terraklene' (paraquat plus simazine) in 1975.

Precautions against Mis-use

In sixteen years of sales world-wide paraquat has caused no fatality or serious injury in normal use. But from time to time people swallow the concentrated formulation, and like many other agricultural chemicals, and indeed some household products, paraquat is poisonous if swallowed. Accidents have invariably occurred because someone has transferred the chemical from its original properly labelled container into a beverage bottle. Incredibly there have been instances where a small quantity of paraquat has been kept in a beer bottle, in a refrigerator!

When this problem became apparent in the mid-1960s warnings were issued to stockists and the public about the dangers of decanting. The label was redesigned to display the warning signs prominently and 'Gramoxone' was scheduled as a poison to permit sales only to professional users. A low-strength granular formulation 'Weedol', is, of course, available for use by amateur gardeners. Research at ICI's Central Toxicology Laboratories into the toxic mode of action of paraquat was intensified and an antidotal treatment was developed. Most victims of accidents from paraquat are now saved, provided they are given this treatment within 24 hours. At the same time research was carried out at Jealott's Hill and Yalding to develop a new formulation of paraquat less likely to be impulsively taken as a drink and safer even if swallowed. The new formulations are now being introduced into the market as fast as registration requirements allow.

Other Bipyridyls

In 1961, in the course of extensive synthetic work in the field of bipyridylium chemistry, attention was drawn to the relationship between herbicidal selectivity and the ease of reduction (measured as redox potential) of many of the compounds. Diquat (redox potential -348 mV) was substantially more selective than was paraquat (redox potential -446 mV) so that it seemed reasonable to look for even greater selectivity in bipyridyls with redox potentials less negative than that of diquat.

A programme of analogue synthesis designed to optimise selectivity produced another candidate for field evaluation, PP745, (redox potential -305 mV). Results of trials carried out in the UK by H M Fox and C R Beech over the next two years were encouraging, and development of PP745, later given the name morfamquat, (**III,** page 68) went into full swing in 1965 and 1966. Field trials programmes took place all over the United Kingdom; independent work was initiated by the NAAS, by Agricultural Colleges in Scotland, and overseas by development teams in Western Europe, North America, South Africa and Australia. The reports on performance which returned to Jealott's Hill amounted to an experimenter's most frustrating dilemma—inconsistency. About a third of the trials produced outstanding weed kills, generating much excitement from the farmers and from the trade, a third were of mediocre performance, satisfactory to the farmer but no advance on the best of currently-available weedkillers and a third were complete failures, the weeds having received little more than a temporary check before resuming their normal growth.

Morfamquat was cleared for limited use on cereals, and was marketed for use on turf, as 'Weedkiller for New Lawns', but erratic performance led to its withdrawal from the sales range after a period of only five years.

Machinery Development

It had been recognised early that the bipyridyls and particularly paraquat had immense potential provided that they could be deposited on the weed and not on the crop. The idea of supplanting the hoe, and even the plough, began to look possible and great benefits could be foreseen in terms of reduced labour costs, erosion control and conservation of moisture. It was also clear that the new technique demanded the development of new machinery.

This recognition coincided with the arrival at Fernhurst of D G Sharp, an engineer from ICI's General Chemicals Division at Runcorn, and the return from West Africa of two others, D A Harris and A Bloomfield, who had been seconded to the Ghana Goverment's cocoa capsid spraying campaign.

The challenge facing the engineers was, literally, the implementation of the technique of direct drilling, or as it was to be called in the USA, 'No-till'; in Australia 'Spray-Seed'; and in Brazil 'Plantio Direto'. At first, it was assumed that a sprayer attached to a drill would suffice, but it was not to be so easy. The sprayer was the least of the problems; existing drills were not robust enough for sowing into uncultivated land and even the 'Sod seeder' drills from Australia failed to give the required performance. With a sense of urgency and excitement every coulter device that could be obtained and others of novel design constructed in the Machinery Department workshops were evaluated in a variety of crop situations. A simple modification to an existing drill might possibly have been adequate for the 'new grass for old' projects then under way but for direct drilling of cereal crops into stubble the simple disc and knife coulter too easily became choked with the 'trash' or débris from the previous crop.

Other workers had found the same problem; and it was solved in much the same way by W A P Bakermans at the Instituut voor Biologisch en Scheikundig Onderzoek in Holland and by P Koronka and his team at Fernhurst by the use of a triple-disc coulter system. This consisted of a single slot-cutting disc followed by paired discs to guide the seed into the slot; and this all-rolling system was able to ride over obstacles or trash that was too heavy.

The two systems were very similar; the Dutch workers were first, but it was the Fernhurst design which, fitted to many proprietary makes of drill, earned wide acclaim as a high speed, low wear system giving minimum soil disturbance. The trials teams were happy but farmers still had to be convinced.

This was done at first by a programme of demonstrations using the few drills constructed at Fernhurst. Later, some fifty drills were manufactured and leased to contractors. With experience, these were modified and improved, awareness of the advantages of direct drilling spread rapidly, and led to acceptance of the direct drill as a common feature of the agricultural scene. Examples of present-day drills are the Bettinson 3-D, the Moore Uni-Drill, the WMF Howard Rotaseeder, the Gibbs Kale drill and the Howard/Stanhay direct drill for maize.

With the provision of reliable and effective seed-placing machinery, attention returned to the sprayer side of the business, and an improved knapsack sprayer was designed, of polypropylene construction, for use in plantations.

With a herbicide as efficient as paraquat, the problem of wind drift was ever present, and a variety of implements was devised, based on the 'dribble bar'. This was nothing more complicated that a gravity fed, rather than pressurised, flow of chemical to a polythene applicator boom. Applicators for specialised use included the 'Arbogard' for ring-weeding young forest trees and the 'Xpando', a pedestrian-operated implement in which one-half of the spray boom telescoped within the other, so adjusting to varying row widths.

The 'Vibro-boom', however, was a major advance in spray technology. In an attempt to reduce still more the volume of application from dribble bars, thus making them suitable for field scale use, the holes in the bar were made smaller and their spacing wider to a point where efficiency started to fall off. To restore efficiency, the dribble bar was vibrated by a cam and cable system. The effect was remarkable and led to the development of the 'Vibro-boom', the first true non-drift system in British agriculture and later to the 'Vibrajet', a miniaturisation of the same system that extended its use to inter-row weed control. This development won for Plant Protection the Burke Trophy, the premier award of the Royal Agricultural Society for new engineering developments. It is used for drift-free application of paraquat and hormone weedkillers and is incorporated in such machines as the 'Uni-row' and the 'Intarow'.

Other specialised equipment ranged from the sophisticated spring-boom tree-base sprayer known as 'Fido', designed for the fruit grower, to a simple vineyard sprayer for use in Eastern Europe, so cheap that it was possible to give it away—that is, to those who bought enough 'Gramoxone'—and various even simpler devices based on a 'peristaltic' pump, such as the 'Polyrow' and 'Vari-row' sprayers designed for local manufacture in countries unable to import the more highly developed machines.

There is no doubt that the inventiveness generated by the novelty of the bipyridyls led to a re-appraisal of many aspects of agricultural technology, and the 'large oak', having grown, has been shedding further 'little acorns' ever since.

References

[1]   Boon W R (1965) 'Diquat and paraquat—new agricultural tools.' *Chemy. Ind.* 8th May, 782–788

[2]   Homer R F, Mees G C, Tomlinson T E (1960) 'Mode of action of dipyridyl quaternary salts as herbicides' *J. Sci. Fd Agric.* **11,** 309–315

[3]   Mees G C (1960) 'Experiments on the herbicide action of 1,1'-ethylene-2,2'-dipyridylium dibromide' *Ann. appl. Biol.* **48,** 601–612

[4]   Headford D W R, Douglas G (1967) 'Tuber necrosis following the destruction of potato foliage with diquat' *Weed Res.* **7** (2) 131–144

[5]   Brian R C (1966) 'The bipyridylium quaternary salts. The effect of atmospheric and soil humidity on the uptake and movement of diquat and paraquat in plants' *Weed Res.* **6** (4) 292–303

[6]   Jeater R S L (1964) 'Evaluation of paraquat and diquat for weed control in rubber' *Weed Res.* **4** (2) 133–141

[7]   Douglas G, Lewis C J, McIlvenny H C (1965) 'The effect of the bipyridyl herbicides on hill communities and their role in the improvement of hill grazing' *J. Br. Grassl. Soc.* **20** (2) 64–71

[8]   Hood A E M, Jameson H R, Cotterell R (1963) 'Destruction of pastures by paraquat as a substitute for ploughing' *Nature, Lond.* **197,** 4869, 381

[9]   Hood A E M (1965) 'Ploughless farming using "Gramoxone"' *Outl. Agric.* **IV, 6,** 286–294

[10] Allen H P (1975) 'ICI Plant Protection Division experience with direct drilling systems 1961–1974' *Outl. Agric.* **8,** 213–215

[11] Calderbank A (1968) 'The bipyridylium herbicides' *Advances in Pest Control Research.* **8,** 127–235. Ed. R L Metcalf. John Wiley & Sons.

Chapter 10

Pyrimidine fungicides

The years 1935 to 1965 saw the introduction of a number of organic fungicides of which the most important were the dithiocarbamates (e.g. thiram, maneb) and the phthalimides (e.g. captan, captafol). Two valuable fungicides developed by ICI during this period are worthy of mention —salicylanilide ('Shirlan') whose fungicidal properties had been discovered by workers at the Shirley Institute, and drazoxolon ('Milcol'). Drazoxolon, discovered at Jealott's Hill in 1959, and discussed in an earlier chapter, is still used as a protectant seed treatment for grasses, peas and beans, and as a spray treatment to control powdery mildew of apples and blackcurrants. The various organic fungicides developed prior to 1965 proved to be superior to earlier sulphur or copper compounds in many situations, either because they were more effective protectants or because they were less damaging to the crop plants. However, their action was still superficial. Like copper and sulphur, they acted at those parts of the plant which are readily accessible to sprays or dusts; they did not halt or cure established infections, and they had to be applied repeatedly in order to replace losses by weathering and to cover the new parts of the plant as they developed.

The possibility of finding fungicidal compounds which could penetrate into and move within the plant was clearly indicated as the best hope of overcoming these difficulties, and substantial programmes of research into systemic fungicides had started at a number of research centres in the 1940s and 1950s. One of the foremost was the Akers Laboratories of ICI, located at Welwyn, Hertfordshire, where P W Brian, S H Crowdy and colleagues investigated the uptake, translocation and antifungal activity of potential systemic chemicals. Much original and useful information on the behaviour of chemicals in plants and soils resulted from these studies. Antibiotics received the most attention, and two, griseofulvin and streptomycin, found some limited use as agricultural fungicides. Disappointingly, however, none of the compounds proved to be sufficiently effective and safe to animals and plants to achieve any real agricultural importance.

Such was the position in the mid-1960s, when a group of pyrimidines with exceptional fungicidal and systemic action was discovered at Jealott's Hill. Quite remarkably, after years of unproductive research in many countries, three major groups of systemic fungicides of great practical value—the 2-aminopyrimidines (ICI), the benzimidazoles (Du Pont), and the oxathiins (Uniroyal)—emerged almost at the same time and subsequently several others of diverse chemical structures appeared. Why the sudden upsurge of useful systemic fungicides after so many barren years? They all showed high contact activity; but it is very doubtful whether any of the initial leads were predictably systemic. Probably, their appearance reflected the enormous increase in the amount of chemical synthesis directed at crop protection which occurred in the 1960s, and the introduction of diseases on plants, rather than fungal cultures on agar plates, as the basis of screening programmes. Research into the 2-aminopyrimidine group of fungicides at Jealott's Hill led to three valuable products—dimethirimol ('Milcurb'), ethirimol ('Milstem', 'Milgo') and bupirimate ('Nimrod').

I   dimethirimol

II   ethirimol

III   bupirimate

Discovery of the pyrimidine group

In the late 1950s various phosphoric acid esters of 2-amino-4-hydroxy-pyrimidines, close analogues of diazinon, were made by V G McHattie and his colleagues at ICI Pharmaceuticals Division for testing as veterinary insecticides. The compounds were active against blowflies and ticks and samples were sent to ICI Australia (then ICI-ANZ) for further tests, and to Jealott's Hill for a fuller evaluation of their biological properties.

As a result of the Australian work, one of these compounds, pyrimithate, was developed and later marketed by Pharmaceuticals Division as the insecticide 'Diothyl', used in the control of animal ectoparasites; it was tested also for other biological properties at ICIANZ's Merrindale research station, where it was shown to possess fungicidal properties including activity against powdery mildew of wheat *(Erysiphe graminis* f. sp. *tritici)* and oat rust *(Puccinia graminis* f. sp. *avenae).* In October 1963 F J D Thomas, then Director of Merrindale, reported these findings to D G Davey of Pharmaceuticals Division and suggested that the compound should be tested in the Jealott's Hill fungicide screen. It had, in fact, been tested by J Stubbs and activity, albeit of a low order, noted. The Pharmaceuticals Division chemists then produced a further seven related compounds, one of which, unremarkable as an insecticide, was exceptionally active as a protectant spray against powdery mildews.

This compound and a few closely-related ones were now shown, by R S Elias and others, to possess not only potent fungicidal activity but the sought-after property of systemic movement as evidenced by a spectacular control of cucumber powdery mildew *(Sphaerotheca fuliginea)* from soil treatment. New analogues were quickly synthesized and tested. There is a corollary to the well-known 'Law of General Cussedness' which states that 'in any series of active compounds the most active will be seen to be the one first discovered, but only after several hundreds more have been tested.' And so it was; striking fungicidal activity was shown against powdery mildews, but none of the new compounds was better than the original lead.

It was then that a second 'break-through' occurred. The original lead, historically essential, was a 'red herring'. B K Snell and R S Elias showed that certain 2-amino-4-hydroxypyrimidines, though lacking a phosphoryl group, nevertheless possessed the same potent systemic fungicidal action against powdery mildews. One of the first of these was dimethirimol (**I,** page 88).

The programme of synthesis of pyrimidines and related compounds lasted, at various levels of intensity, for over seven years. Ethirimol, (**II,** page 88) appeared in 1966, just a year after the synthetic work had started.

Fungicidal activity was not confined to the 2-amino-4-hydroxy-pyrimidines; related compounds made by P F H Freeman and B K Snell included 4-mercapto, 4-alkylthio, 4-hydrazino, 4-amino, and certain 4-alkoxy pyrimidines, which showed similar, though somewhat lower, fungicidal activity. As candidates for development, however, such compounds were unattractive on cost/efficiency grounds. The insecticides pirimiphos-methyl and pirimiphos-ethyl, reviewed in the next chapter, also stemmed from this programme of fungicide synthesis.

The preparation of a series of non-toxic esters (O-acyl) of the hydroxy-pyrimidines produced certain benzoates, carbonates, and phosphonic acid esters which showed excellent protectant and fumigant activity against powdery mildew in the glasshouse. Structure/activity correlations were followed to produce compounds of enhanced activity but, unfortunately, under field conditions none of these compounds was sufficiently persistent to warrant commercial development. Sulphonic acid esters, however, made later in the course of this work, were highly active against apple mildew in glasshouse tests. In the field they showed the combined properties of excellent activity, penetration and adequate persistence, which made them the group of choice from which to select a candidate fungicide for development on apples, and so emerged bupirimate, (**III,** page 88), the third 'pyrimidine fungicide'.

The discovery of these fungicides, though to some extent fortuitous, reflects the importance of good observation, good communication and the right range of screening tests. Without a powdery mildew in the primary screen the very specific fungicidal activity of the hydroxypyrimidines would have been missed. Neither the selective antifungal activity nor the systemic properties of this particular group of pyrimidines could have been predicted on the basis of biochemical knowledge available at the time, or even now. K J Bent has shown that the pyrimidines directly and specifically inhibit the growth of powdery mildew fungi [1]. They can affect various stages of development such as spore germination, hyphal elongation or sporulation. It is notable that both dimethirimol and ethirimol applied to the roots can stop the growth of powdery mildews before they penetrate the leaf surface; thus the fungicide must pass through the surface of the leaf into the fungus. The site of action of these fungicides in target organisms is still a matter for conjecture; unfortunately powdery mildews, being obligate parasites, are extremely difficult subjects for biochemical investigation.

Dimethirimol

The discovery of dimethirimol was followed by an intensive programme of evaluation in laboratory and glasshouse. Dimethirimol was shown to be translocated in the xylem stream; although it was effective when applied to cucumber leaves, stems or roots, a unique long-term protection resulted from application to the soil. Taken up by the roots, along with water and nutrients, the fungicide passed upwards to the transpiring leaves which were thereby protected from mildew. The soil acted as a reservoir supplying the compound to the plant over a long period so that new leaves were protected as they developed. For this process to be sustained, the soil in which the chemical was held had to be kept continually moist.

Results of the first commercial glasshouse trial, carried out by Ann Cole in 1966, exceeded everyone's expectations. Dimethirimol, applied to the soil at the base of the cucumber stem, not only gave complete control of mildew for the whole season and resulted in a substantial and very valuable increase in yield, but residues in the fruit were less than 0·2 parts per million. Performance of this kind was hitherto unknown, and heralded a new era in fungicide treatment.

A rapid review of the world requirement for mildew control in cucurbits by E M Godbold at Fernhurst revealed that such a fungicide was badly needed for use in cucumber glasshouses in Europe and in the irrigated melon fields of the Mediterranean region.

In 1967 Claire Shephard, with J Paul at Jealott's Hill and colleagues from SOPRA in France and Zeltia Agraria in Spain undertook an intensive programme of co-operator trials in the three countries to ascertain the best method and rate of application under the different cultural conditions.

In the meantime, research into methods of manufacture was proceeding at Dyestuffs Division (now Organics Division). By the beginning of 1968 a pilot plant was producing small but significant quantities of 'PP 675' as the compound was then known. Extensive environmental and toxicological studies at Jealott's Hill and at ICI's Central Toxicology Laboratories in Cheshire were drawing to a close and indicated a high level of safety. The compound was registered for use on commercial cucumbers, and sales began in April 1968.

The new compound aroused a great deal of interest among growers both in UK and elsewhere. By August 1968 dimethirimol had proved itself in a variety of commercial situations as the first, highly successful, soil applied fungicide for control of a foliage disease and, in 1969, commercial use was extended to Holland and Israel under the trade name 'Milcurb', again with excellent results. Commercial use in Spain began in 1970 in melon fields, where the chemical was applied as a granule in the irrigation channels.

The following year a serious set-back occurred. Reports from Holland and the UK indicated that the treatment was not effective. The product was examined and found to be up to specification. However, on testing the mildews from several glasshouses in Holland, it was found that they had changed in sensitivity, so that a greatly increased dose of dimethirimol was now needed to give control [2]. These mildews were found to be widespread in Holland and Germany so, after only a very short life in these countries, the product had to be withdrawn and growers elsewhere were warned that they might run into the same problem. At this point the whole future of this remarkable young fungicide seemed in jeopardy. Such a rapid development of resistance would have been astonishing among insects; it was totally without precedent in fungal populations. The few known instances of resistance to fungicides had occurred only after prolonged use; the new compound had run into problems in Holland in only the second year of general use. It was not clear whether strains of the troublesome mildews were present in the original population and had multiplied due to lack of competition from sensitive strains, or whether they had originated spontaneously during this short period of use. Their simultaneous widespread appearance suggested that they arose independently at a number of points.

The position has been watched closely and it is now reassuring to see that dimethirimol is still effective in most of the countries where it was introduced in the late 1960s. Furthermore its use has extended to many other countries, as, for example, Japan, where most of the melon crop is now treated successfully.

The risk of resistance arising probably varies with the pattern of usage of the compound; extensive year-round application under glasshouse conditions as occurred in NW Europe, was undoubtedly most favourable for the emergence of resistant mildew strains. The prediction of such events remains difficult, if not impossible.

Since 1970 the frequency of occurrence of the less fungicidally sensitive mildews in Holland appears to have declined, but they still occur occasionally. In the UK, dimethirimol has now been reintroduced, following the appearance of resistance to other fungicides. It is usually used alternately with a totally different material, in the hope that strains which are not sensitive to one compound will succumb to the other. So far this approach has been very successful and seems to be a developing trend for the fungicidal strategy of the future.

Ethirimol

Although powdery mildew had long been recognised as commonly occurring on barley and wheat in most major growing areas, as late as the 1960s there was little information on the extent of yield losses attributable to the disease. The results of Jealott's Hill field experiments with drazoxolon in 1965/66, and official surveys carried out by the Ministry of Agriculture from 1967 onwards, first indicated that yield losses of 10–20% were frequent. Nevertheless, market surveys suggested that there was little commercial opportunity for the chemical control of mildew and, in this uncertain situation, considerable faith was needed to embark on the development of a new fungicide for use on cereals.

Dimethirimol had been tested against barley mildew in the field by R M Bebbington in 1966. It was applied as a spray in combination with a hormone weedkiller, as a seed treatment, and as soil-incorporated granules. Each method of application gave very good disease control, but there was some phytotoxicity and yield increases were disappointingly small.

By the next year ethirimol, the mono-ethyl analogue of dimethirimol, had become the favoured candidate. In the glasshouse, it had given similar results to dimethirimol when applied as a spray, and much better results as a soil treatment. It was less phytotoxic to cereal plants, and it appeared to be potentially cheaper. In the field, applied as a seed dressing or as a coated fertilizer granule combine-drilled with the seed, almost season-long disease control was obtained. Spray applications were moderately effective but as they were far less persistent than seed/soil applications and clearly did not fully exploit the remarkable systemic properties of the new compound they were relegated to second place in the subsequent development programme. A small trial on winter barley laid down late in 1967 established that disease control could persist until the spring, but the main thrust of further development, led by D H Brooks, took place in spring 1968.

Because of the difficulty of correlating yield increases with disease control, particularly in small plots, the 1968 trials programme adopted a plot size of one acre in an attempt to minimise re-invasion by disease from untreated areas. These trials showed that greatly improved disease control was obtained in the large plots, and confirmed that both seed treatment and combine-drilled granules (though not broadcast granules) gave excellent disease control; they also demonstrated, for the first time under commercial field conditions, that control of severe mildew resulted in development of a more extensive root system, a greater number of tillers and an increase in grain size [3] [4]. These observations stimulated considerable interest at university and other research stations and, unusually for a chemical at this stage of development, samples of ethirimol were offered to university workers in several West and East European countries and in the USA. The objective was to learn more about the chemical but, incidentally, new light was shed on the effect of the organic fraction of soils in reducing activity of such chemicals, and the enhancement of malting quality which resulted from the control of mildew. Ethirimol was also supplied to the UK Ministry of Agriculture for use in their National Disease Survey, and this did much to bring to public attention the potential gains from controlling mildew.

Trials carried out in 1969 by Plant Protection staff and numerous co-operators refined knowledge on rates and methods of application, varietal response, effect of soil type and moisture status; whilst studies went ahead on the toxicology, ecology, residue analysis, synthesis and formulation of the product. A programme of work was also started to modify or build machines capable of applying the necessarily relatively large amounts of chemical to the seed. To co-ordinate the many facets of the work, a multi-disciplinary project team was formed. Under Brooks' leadership this team proved to be an excellent way of securing orderly and speedy progress and set a pattern which is still followed; its objective was to launch ethirimol in the UK and a number of European countries late in 1970, for application as a seed dressing or spray on the 1971 spring barley crop. Work on coated fertilizer granules was abandoned because of difficulties in exploiting this method commercially. Thus, by the end of the second year of development, most of the properties and methods of use of ethirimol were understood; but there were still many technical and commercial difficulties to tackle. N Grabham and R C Clinch had shown that a 'col' formulation provided excellent retention of the chemical on the seed, and was compatible with other seed treatments normally used (the 'col', in practice, acted as a sticker for the other treatments). Initially, great difficulty was found in formulating ethirimol consistently as a stable 'col'. It was soon revealed that the chemical existed in several crystal forms, only one of which was suitable for 'col' formulation; by making changes in the final stages of the manufacturing process the correct polymorph was obtained.

The 'col' was too viscous for application in standard machines, but J E Elsworth and colleagues in the Machinery Development Group at Fernhurst had invented a relatively simple device which could be used to make the 'Plantector' suitable.

Conversion kits were fitted to over fifty merchants' machines during autumn 1970. Because of a tendency for the chemical to accumulate in the machine, it was necessary to have very long experimental runs. In one test some 70 tons of seed was treated and this was put to good use in what was probably the largest fungicide trial ever conducted. In conjunction with the UK Agricultural Development and Advisory Service, all winter barley in a 20,000 acre area of N Norfolk was drilled with treated seed. The area, bounded on two sides by sea, was observed intensively by ADAS staff to see whether, by preventing carry-over of the disease on winter barley, the subsequent epidemic on spring barley in the vicinity could be delayed. The experiment received wide press and television publicity but, although the degree of infection on the winter barley was greatly reduced, effects on the progress of the disease in the spring barley were, in fact, surprisingly small.

Machinery problems continued. Seed treated with ethirimol flowed less easily and, in consequence, merchants had to be persuaded to market treated barley in larger (oat) sacks, and farmers had to be warned to recalibrate their seed drills, as work at Jealott's Hill had shown that reducing the seed rate impaired disease control.

Experience in practice has confirmed the results obtained during this period. Yield increases from seed-dressing treatments of spring barley have averaged at least 10%, covering the cost of chemical and application some three to four times. 'Milstem' has become well established in Europe—in 1976 over 40% of UK spring barley seed was 'Milstem' treated. It has proved to be especially valuable in Scotland, where the variety 'Golden Promise' is favoured. This is an excellent malting barley which is, however, very susceptible to mildew; its present success in Scotland can be attributed largely to the protection afforded by 'Milstem' seed treatment. On winter barley, excellent control of autumn attacks of disease was obtained from seed treatment; control persisted until the spring, sometimes with remarkable effects on the vigour of the crop [5]; but subsequent studies (described later) suggest that this treatment is inadvisable.

On winter wheat in Hungary and the USA, seed treatments gave good control of disease on young plants in the autumn, but the effect was not persistent enough to control the later infections which are generally of greater importance in wheat crops.

Continuing investigations into the factors affecting the performance of sprays, by T J Purnell and R V Offield and, later, by N G Buckley led to the improved formulation 'Milgo', effective now against mildews of both barley and wheat. Many seasons of work have been necessary to optimise performance on wheat in West Europe, where, unlike barley, it generally seems necessary to control disease on the flag leaf in order to give the best yield increases. 'Milgo' is now widely used on wheat in Europe, and extensive trials have been carried out elswhere including Canada, the USA and Brazil. However, in wheat, other diseases often occur in a complex with mildew, and special mixtures have been devised to give a broad spectrum of activity. For example, 'Milcap', developed by a team led by J E Varley, is a 'col' formulation of ethirimol mixed with captafol for combined control of *Septoria* and mildew.

On barley, 'Milgo' is used to a much smaller extent than is 'Milstem', but if application is correctly timed a good yield increase can be obtained from the spray, and it is useful in various situations where seed has not been treated; examples are areas or varieties where the risk of mildew infection is low, and on fields where the soil has a high organic matter content and hence is unsuitable for a seed treatment.

In 1972, strains of mildew resistant to ethirimol were isolated under greenhouse conditions. Plant Protection had been monitoring field populations since 1970, but the rapid spread of dimethirimol-resistant strains in commercial glasshouses indicated that the sensitivity to ethirimol of mildew isolates from UK barley fields ought to be more comprehensively surveyed.

Such investigations were carried out by workers at Jealott's Hill [6] and jointly by the Plant Breeding Institute and ADAS during the years 1973–75, and they showed that partially-resistant strains could be found surviving for a time in treated fields. The more highly resistant forms, whilst apparently rare and transient, would be difficult to control if they became abundant early in the season; for this reason the recommendation for the use of 'Milstem' on winter barley was discontinued, so as to decrease the period of exposure to the fungicide, and hence the selection pressure exerted by it. This strategy has ensured that a high level of performance of the product is still being maintained.

In 1973 ICI Plant Protection gained the Queens Award to Industry—its first for 'technical innovation'—for the development of 'Milstem'.

Bupirimate

As the third member of the fungicidal pyrimidine family to be discovered, bupirimate was shorn of some of the excitement of the original 'breakthrough'. Its discovery was the result of a long, methodical, and target-oriented research programme, and it represented the 'hat-trick' for the team of synthetic chemists and biologists involved.

Apple powdery mildew, caused by the fungus *Podosphaera leucotricha*, is a serious problem limiting crop production and quality in many apple-growing areas throughout the world. Its dramatic increase in severity during the 1950s and 1960s was partly due to a change in pruning practice, from the old but labour-intensive system in which overwintering mildewed tips were removed, to renewal pruning which removed only cankered and crossing branches. But it was also due to the replacement of lime-sulphur by more effective, more agreeable and less phytotoxic scab fungicides such as captan which, unlike lime-sulphur, were not effective against mildew. Elemental sulphur and dinocap became established as standard mildew control treatments; both proved inadequate to contain the disease in many orchards, including the expertly managed Surney orchard at Fernhurst, where mildew developed into a serious problem on apples despite frequent and thorough spray applications.

The market opportunity for a compound giving improved control of apple mildew was well appreciated within ICI, and screening tests had been conducted at Jealott's Hill since the 1950s. The first significant lead occurred following the synthesis in 1960 of drazoxolon. Indeed, following a series of UK field programmes from 1962–66, this compound showed sufficient promise to justify a commercial recommendation, and it is sold (as 'Milcol') in warmer countries such as Israel where its better eradicant activity compared to dinocap is particularly useful. But, in the UK, a similar recommendation had to be withdrawn because the product induced russetting of fruit in years when the spring weather was particularly wet and cold.

By 1964 the pyrimidines had appeared, and there were high hopes that either ethirimol or dimethirimol, which showed outstanding activity on other powdery mildews, would be similarly effective against mildew on apple. In field trials programmes in 1967/8, however, mildew control with the pyrimidines proved to be little better than that with dinocap or the newer standard binapacryl and the degree of fruit russetting with ethirimol was unacceptable.

The continuing programme of chemical synthesis in the pyrimidine group was rewarded in 1969 when, in a series of glasshouse tests, J A W Turner and P M Lyne discovered that certain sulphamoyl derivatives were superior to other pyrimidines against apple mildew. Subsequent field tests in the UK, Australia and Spain from 1970–73 confirmed the outstanding activity of various members of the group and culminated in the selection of bupirimate for development, primarily as an apple mildew fungicide, for world-wide use [7]. Again, the multi-disciplinary project team approach was used; this team, led by J R Finney, for the first time at Jealott's Hill made use of modified critical path scheduling techniques. Whilst these were disparagingly referred to by sceptics as 'Underground (railway) maps' they proved to be highly successful in co-ordinating activities, by now considerably complicated by the requirements of registration authorities.

A large evaluation/development programme was launched in most important apple-growing countries to optimise the rate and frequency of application and to study the influence of formulation and interactions with variety and environmental conditions. The trials confirmed excellent control of both primary and secondary mildew, including significant eradicant activity, coupled with good fruit finish. There is no doubt that the marked vapour and translaminar effects, which had been demonstrated by G M Farrell and Mary Turner in experiments under controlled conditions, contributed to this performance. There were no adverse effects on predator mite populations so that the compound was of immediate interest for integrated control programmes.

A Division-wide competition for a trade name—another 'first' for the project—was won by H G Dowden (for 30 years the farm engineer at Jealott's Hill) for his 'Nimrod', (the 'mighty hunter' of the Old Testament), from a total list of over two thousand contributions. 'Nimrod' achieved limited first sales in 1975 in the UK and several other countries, and rapidly attracted favourable attention from growers and advisory workers worldwide; in terms of biological performance and environmental safety it is probably the most advanced product available for use against apple mildew.

The development programme was not without drama. Commercial apple growers are, understandably, highly sensitive to any suspected risk of crop damage from spray chemicals. In some early field experiments where relatively high rates of bupirimate were used in order to define safety margins, there were instances of premature defoliation. It was later found, with considerable relief, that these were confined to a few varieties, of which only Cox and Jonathan were of general commercial importance, and then only when trees were suffering from water stress. In subsequent development work, and in commercial practice, recommended rates proved to be effective and safe, even during the extremely dry summer of 1976.

Whilst bupirimate was developed principally as an apple mildew

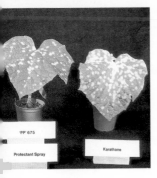

'PP' 675

Protectant Spray

Karathane

3

Pyrimidine fungicides

1 Applying 'Milcurb' granules to melons, Spain
2 Pot test with PP 675 ('Milcurb')
3 Apple primary mildew
4 Spraying 'Nimrod' on apples, Italy

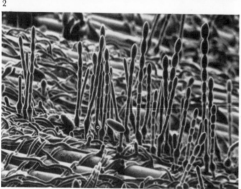

Pyrimidine fungicides

1 Spraying 'Milgo' on barley
  to control mildew
2 Mildew on barley
3 Electron micrograph (× 180)
4 Mildew on barley of causal
  organism (left) untreated and
  (right) protected by 'Milstem'

fungicide it also gives excellent control of many other powdery mildews, and it is now used commercially on roses, cucurbits and peaches. Of these, rose mildew is probably the most important, and bupirimate has proved to be a highly successful treatment on both indoor and outdoor varieties.

References

[1] Bent K J (1970) 'Fungitoxic action of dimethirimol and ethirimol' *Ann. appl. Biol.* **66,** 103–13

[2] Bent K J, Cole A M, Turner J A W, Woolner M (1971) 'Resistance of cucumber powdery mildew to dimethirimol' *Proc. 6th Br. Insectic. Fungic. Conf.* 274–82

[3] Brooks D H (1970) 'Powdery mildew of barley and its control' *Outl. Agric.* **6,** 122–7

[4] Brooks D H (1972) 'Observations on the effects of mildew, *Erysiphe graminis,* on growth of spring and winter barley' *Ann. appl. Biol.* **70,** 149–56

[5] Finney J R, Hall D W (1972) 'The effect of an autumn attack of mildew *(Erisyphe graminis)* on the growth and development of winter barley' *Pl. Path.* **21,** 73–6

[6] Shephard M C, Bent K J, Woolner M, Cole A M (1975) 'Sensitivity to ethirimol of powdery mildew from UK barley crops' *Proc. 8th Br. Insectic. Fungic. Conf.* 59–66

[7] Finney J R, Farrell G M, Bent K J (1975) 'Bupirimate—a new fungicide for the control of powdery mildews on apples and other crops' *Proc. 8th Br. Insectic. Fungic Conf.* 667–74

Chapter 11

Pyrimidine insecticides

Knowledge of the mechanism of action of the enzyme acetylcholinesterase, particularly at its active centre, accumulated during the 1950s and early 1960s and it became possible to build-up schemes (albeit crude) for the way in which the enzyme caused hydrolysis of acetylcholine. This, in turn, made it possible for chemists to attempt a semi-rational design of compounds capable of inhibiting or blocking the enzyme, and, particularly in the years 1964–67, a great many compounds synthesised at Jealott's Hill demonstrated broad-spectrum insecticidal activity of a high order in laboratory and greenhouse tests. The criteria for field evaluation, however, had become more exacting, toxicological studies more refined, and the need for target-oriented testing better understood.

When, in 1964, a number of phosphoric acid esters of pyrimidines made at ICI Pharmaceuticals Division as veterinary insecticides arrived at Jealott's Hill, the insecticide screen was more than fully occupied with a large group of novel organophosphorus compounds recently synthesised there. So many of these compounds showed high insecticidal activity in primary tests, that the small group of pyrimidine phosphates arriving at such a time, seemed to be an *embarras de richesse,* and was greeted with little enthusiasm. This group showed quite high, but unexciting, activity against test insects representative of crop pests, though one, pyrimithate, was later marketed by Pharmaceuticals Division as 'Diothyl', for the control of ectoparasites of farm animals. They also showed fungicidal activity, and this did excite immediate interest at Jealott's Hill, as the previous chapter has shown. The subsequent fungicide synthesis programme, whilst it produced no noteworthy organophosphorus fungicide, provided a rich vein of compounds for testing when, in 1966, the insecticide programme needed a change of direction. Using rudimentary knowledge of the mode of action of organophosphorus and carbamate insecticides, and following such precedents as existed in the biochemical and patent literature, B K Snell and S P Sharpe attempted to correlate the chemical structures of the pyrimidine insecticides with their biological activity. At first, this was done on a semi-empirical basis, since facilities were not then available for the correlation of biological activity with physical parameters, such as partition co-efficients, acidity or basicity, molecular conformations and other properties that, nowadays, help the chemist to predict activity in molecules as yet unmade.

It was observed that high insecticidal activity was largely confined to those compounds in which substituents R^1 to R^4 (**I**, page 102) were hydrogen or lower alkyl (up to six carbon atoms). Further increase in the size of the substituent led to markedly reduced activity. Broad-spectrum insecticidal activity fell off rapidly as the size of the group R^4 was increased beyond two carbon atoms. Thus, within the series of phosphorylated pyrimidines, structural requirements for high insecticidal activity differed from those for high fungicidal activity, (a 5-butyl substituent, $R^4=C_4H_9$ gave optimum activity against powdery mildews: see previous chapter), whereupon the two chemical research programmes diverged.

Substitution at the 2-position (NR^1R^2) could be varied to a limited extent with retention of good insecticidal activity. 2-Aminopyrimidines (**I**, where $NR^1R^2=NH_2$), were highly active, but too toxic to mammals to warrant extensive investigation. Several compounds prepared by I T Kay, notably a 2-acylaminopyrimidine, were extensively field tested over a number of years. In the event, the simple 2-dialkylamino-substituted compounds were judged to be the most active, and the dimethylamino and diethylamino compounds were finally preferred. Consideration of likely manufacturing costs led to the favouring of pyrimidines unsubstituted $(R^3=H)$, or having a methyl substituent $(R^3=CH_3)$ at the 6-position, although insecticidal activity was by no means limited to such structures; and to the eventual development of pirimiphos-ethyl (**II**) and pirimiphos-methyl (**III**).

The final selection of these two compounds was the culmination of a vast screening programme led by F L C Baranyovits and Joan Masters. This was followed by a painstaking appraisal of all the properties on which the success of a crop protection chemical depends, for which G C Mees was largely responsible. These include, in addition to intrinsic activity, persistence on plants and in soil, vapour and systemic action, safety to plants and animals and the probable ease of manufacture and cost. The field evaluation of the two pyrimidine phosphates involved an entomological 'campaign' of a complexity and world scale never before attempted at Jealott's Hill, and meanwhile, a third pyrimidine insecticide, the aphid-specific carbamate pirimicarb, had emerged from a parallel synthetic programme.

The development of pirimicarb will be described later in this chapter, although, because of its readily defined usage, it was the first of the three to reach the market.

Pirimiphos-methyl ('Actellic')

From the beginning, pirimiphos-methyl was seen to be a broad-spectrum insecticide with acaricidal properties, but so were a very considerable number of analogous compounds tested at that time. When mammalian toxicity tests showed that it was also an outstandingly safe compound (oral LD_{50} to rat was some 2000 mg/kg), a more detailed examination of its properties was, clearly, called for.

The problem in introducing a new broad spectrum product of any kind, is to identify a reasonably small number of markets in which it offers the user some advantage. These must collectively add up to a size that justifies the cost of the introduction—the money spent on field trials, safety testing, manufacture of the new chemical, and the market launch. The number of identified outlets must not be too large or effort will be dissipated and costs may rise to an unacceptable level.

The introduction of pirimiphos-methyl was peculiarly difficult for Plant Protection Ltd which was, in the late 1960s, still a relatively small company, fairly experienced wtih herbicides, but without much detailed knowledge of either the main insect problems around the world, or the strengths and weaknesses of the chemicals used to control them. Moreover, the property of safety to man, which was the advantage that pirimiphos-methyl could, from the start, be seen to possess, was not one that was easily sold to users who had become very accustomed to handling more toxic products with little apparent risk.

The programme to identify markets was prolonged. Indeed, some ten years after pirimiphos-methyl was first discovered, it is still in being. It is not surprising that there was, within the Company, opposition to its con-tinuance when, after some years, foreseeable sales were still small, and it can be fairly said that the survival of the embryo product for a long time depended more on faith than on logic.

A turning point came in 1974, when high farm prices in the USA, coupled with increased costs of oil-based chemical feedstocks, indirectly created an unusually high demand for crop protection chemicals, forcing up prices. Pirimiphos-methyl suddenly began to look much more cost-competitive with established products, at a time when sufficient knowledge of its properties had accumulated to enable it to be marketed with conviction.

The story had begun in the glasshouse, where tests with insects exposed on treated plants at various times after spraying had shown that the persistence of pirimiphos-methyl on crops was likely to be short. Fumigant activity from sprayed leaf surfaces was high, and was subsequently demonstrated to be an important cause of the lack of persistence. Application to the soil in which plants were growing did not affect insects feeding on the leaves, so pirimiphos-methyl was obviously not systemic. Bioassay of treated soil also indicated that persistence there was too short for the compound to make a successful soil insecticide. So, for agricultural use, it looked as though it was necessary to find markets where foliar treatments to control pest complexes, and short persistence of chemical residues, were important. Aerial application could be considered because of the low toxicity of the compound, and formulation characteristics also indicated that ultra-low-volume (ULV) spraying, advantageous for other insecticides, was a possibility.

However, the laboratory evaluation against flies and mosquitoes involved spraying the chemical onto wooden plaques. Surprisingly, on this biologically inert surface, persistence for up to six months was recorded, suggesting that pirimiphos-methyl might succeed in the public health field. Similar persistence on dry seeds indicated the control of stored product pests as a target.

Mees' logical approach, which had led to the selection of the compounds of choice, was now succeeded by the logistical talents of J H Proctor, a field entomologist of global experience, first with the, then, Empire Cotton Growing Corporation and later with the Overseas Development Department of Plant Protection at Fernhurst.

The evaluation programme at first concentrated on agricultural and horticultural outlets, where the nature and variety of the trials were such that special areas of responsibility were impossible; and the Jealott's Hill entomologists worked loosely, but effectively, as a team. Baranyovits and Joan Masters carried out much of the work on aphids, whiteflies and scales, other commitments being divided between P Rivett, F C Peacock and Proctor himself, later joined by C N E Ruscoe and D D Evans; but there was considerable overlapping and the involvement of staff in ICI's overseas subsidiary and associated companies and that of numerous official bodies was vital. Aerial applications and ULV trials drew heavily on the expertise of M R Middleton of Formulation Section and R Merrett of the Machinery Development Group.

One line of work investigated the control of whiteflies. Strains of the glasshouse whitefly *Trialeurodes vaporariorum* had become resistant to DDT, malathion and other products in common use, and pirimiphos-methyl controlled these well. After an early attempt to make smoke generators had run into difficulties, emphasis switched to the technique of fogging, in which the insecticide is volatilised in a solvent and condenses into a fog. Trials by A McCracken proved highly successful and, along with conventional spraying, the treatment was widely adopted in the UK and overseas.

This development directed attention to uses against other whitefly species in the field, of which the most striking success was in Turkey where, by 1974, *Bemisia tabaci* had become an extremely serious pest in cotton. Turkish workers showed pirimiphos-methyl to be more effective on the nymphs than dimethoate, and large scale markets quickly developed there and in other countries.

Results on aphids were less spectacular, though this was of little importance because concurrent work was establishing pirimicarb as an outstanding new aphicide. In general, it was found that where pirimiphos-methyl was directed against pest complexes, aphids were adequately controlled.

Other Hemiptera such as scale insects and mealy bugs were also generally well controlled, as were the Pentatomids *Aelia* and *Eurygaster* on wheat, by aerial ULV applications. On the other hand, successful control of certain beetle and caterpillar pests required a longer persistence on foliage than pirimiphos-methyl could give. Thus, much effort was put into trials on codling moth on apples in Southern France without commercially acceptable protection being achieved at competitive rates of application. Fortunately, work done at the same time showed that aerial ULV applications could control other caterpillars in trees, such as *Tortrix viridiana* on oaks and the olive moth *Prays oleellus*. This lead was later exploited in the highly successful development of techniques to control the date-palm moth *Batrachedra amydraula* by workers in Iraq. Pirimiphos-methyl fitted the Iraqi situation well, because there were edible crops and houses beneath the palms, and only the safest of insecticides could be considered.

I

II   pirimiphos-methyl

III   pirimiphos-ethyl

IV

V   pirimicarb

Another pest well controlled by pirimiphos-methyl was the sugar-beet weevil *Bothynoderes punctiventris*. Large scale applications in the USSR confirmed its effectiveness against this pest, a result which was predicted after early development trials against the pygmy-mangold beetle *Atomaria linearis,* of similar habit, had proved successful. Another important beetle pest, the cotton-boll weevil *Anthonomus grandis,* however, required uneconomically high rates of application, possibly because of losses by volatilisation at high temperatures.

Thus, as experience was gained in the use of pirimiphos-methyl in a variety of crop/pest situations, early misgivings about its short persistence on plants gave way to the realisation that this, together with its safety in use was, in fact, the strong point of the compound. Whilst control of some insects is unspectacular, the product is effective against most pest complexes and it has no lasting effect on beneficial insect populations; it may be applied right up to and throughout harvesting of the produce and it can be applied safely by farm workers unused to handling toxic materials. Pirimiphos-methyl is, at present, a newcomer to the agricultural scene [1], but it is predicted that, with increasing use, it will be seen to be both 'broad-spectrum' and environmentally acceptable, properties which have hitherto generally been regarded as incompatible.

Use in Public Health

The plywood plaque test which directed attention to the public health possibilities of pirimiphos-methyl was the first stage in an elaborate sequence developed by the World Health Organisation (WHO) for selecting chemicals for the control of mosquito vectors of malaria and other disease-carrying insects.

Subsequent development, largely the work of J McCallum Deighton and R Pickering, was heavily dependent on the co-operation of Institutes and individuals in many parts of the world. Over a period of seven years, pirimiphos-methyl has progressed through all stages of the WHO programme and is now seen to be an effective and safe replacement for DDT, to which mosquito resistance is increasingly widespread.

As well as carrying disease, biting mosquitoes are a nuisance; early Jealott's Hill work against 'nuisance' pests examined aerial fogging and ULV spray applications in both Malaysia and Yugoslavia, while ground ULV applications have been tested by university workers in the USA. The results of all trials add up to the conclusion that pirimiphos-methyl is some three times as active as malathion against adult mosquitoes and greatly superior on the larvae [2]. The larvicidal advantage has been confirmed by Russian work.

Another line of public health work pursued by M R Parham in Germany demonstrated the persistence of the chemical in tests on cockroaches, and led eventually to the development of specially-formulated sprays for local authorities and public health contractors, and of an aerosol for domestic use. The broad spectrum of activity and safety of the compound made such an aerosol generally useful against flies, fleas, bed bugs, earwigs, scorpions, wasps, spiders and other unwelcome domestic visitors.

Pirimiphos-methyl has also been shown to be highly suitable for the large scale control of flies by municipalities in problem areas, such as the Middle East. In the early 1970s, street fogging trials were conducted with the co-operation of the authorities in Damascus and Baghdad, and similarly, in Amman, ground sprays were tested on refuse dumps and other breeding sites. Later, large commercial possibilities emerged with the adoption by central administrations, such as those in Saudi Arabia, of town-scale spraying programmes by aerial contractors. To develop this type of outlet, a most ambitious trial was undertaken, in which three towns in Saudi Arabia were treated aerially with pirimiphos-methyl ULV for a month, while ground sprays were applied to rubbish dumps, slaughter houses and other breeding sites. This work involved a team of over a dozen ICI staff drawn from Fernhurst employing, with the assistance of local authorities, techniques derived largely from the Jealott's Hill work. It was highly successful and future developments in public health areas are now largely a matter of commerce.

Control of Stored-products Pests

The safety and type of activity of pirimiphos-methyl presented the challenging prospect of marketing the first new stored-products insecticide since the advent of malathion over ten years ago. It was clearly necessary to involve university laboratories and official organisations in this work as early as possible, and the investigation of residues in treated produce had to be co-ordinated with a toxicological programme expanded to accommodate this highly specialised application. The necessarily protracted development programme, in the hands of McCallum Deighton and R Pascoe, was given a degree of topicality by the increasingly widespread occurrence of malathion-resistant strains of stored-product pests, against which pirimiphos-methyl was very active.

It was first necessary to characterise fully the properties of the chemical in stored-products usage. It had high biological activity against beetles, moths and mites, and early admixture trials with grain showed a long period of protection against infestation. It showed similar persistence when applied to structural materials or hessian bags, yet a very early trial also identified fumigant activity against the weevil *Sitophilus granarius* kept close to, but not in contact with, treated grain. Laboratory trials further demonstrated longer persistence than malathion when admixed with grain, particularly at high temperature and grain moisture content.

With this information, it was possible to initiate large-scale grain admixture trials in England, and a great number of co-operators overseas also undertook trials, with which in many instances Jealott's Hill staff were involved. Investigations in France showed that pirimiphos-methyl gave a degree of control of immature stages of pests within the grain, and this opened up the exciting possibility of use, not only for the protection of clean grain from infestation, but also of disinfestation, with pirimiphos-methyl used as a replacement for fumigation [3]. The French result was confirmed in laboratory work at Jealott's Hill, showing that fewer adults emerged from treated grain. Their reproduction was effectively prevented, bringing the infestation to an end.

The story can go no further in this book. Clearly, the use of a pesticide in and around foodstuffs must be extremely carefully controlled, and registration and approval for such use very properly takes a long time. The FAO Expert Committee on pesticide residues has recommended tolerances for pirimiphos-methyl ranging from 2–20 ppm in various grain products; commercial clearances have now been obtained for its use for disinfestation and/or admixture with grains in the UK and a number of other countries, and work is continuing towards the wider registration of what is believed to be an extremely safe and effective material.

Pyrimidine insecticides

Aerial fogging with 'Actellic' for
mosquito control

Pyrimidine insecticides

1 Spraying olives with 'Actellic'
2 'Actellifog' in tomatoes
3 Olive fly damage
4 White fly adult and scales
5 White fly on tomato
6 'Primicid' to control banana
  weevil, West Indies
7 'Actellic' smoke in plastic tunnel

Pyrimidine insecticides

1 Aphid damage to peach twig
2 Spraying peaches, with
   'Pirimor', Italy
3 F L C Baranyovits
4 R Ghosh
5 Aphids on wheat
6 Spraying cereal crop with
   'Aphox'

3

4

5

6

2

1 Cocoa capsid spraying, Ghana
2 Rice trial, Spain
3 Cereal plots, Australia

3

Pirimiphos-ethyl ('Primicid')

First synthesised in 1965, pirimiphos-ethyl was one of the first members of the pyrimidine 'family' to be screened.

With a spectrum of activity and physical characteristics similar to those of pirimiphos-methyl, but a less favourable toxicity (oral LD_{50} to rat of 140–200 mg/kg), pirimiphos-ethyl exhibited one important and desirable difference—the property of persistence in the soil.

In the Jealott's Hill soil assay test it showed a high degree of insecticidal activity over a period of three to six months. It was particularly effective on flies and beetles, the principal soil pests, and because it was generally of low phytotoxicity, its use as a seed treatment could be envisaged.

The two pyrimidine phosphates were thus seen to complement one another and, together with the specific aphicide pirimicarb, to constitute a neat insecticide 'package'.

Early evaluation, which included field trials in New Zealand, where grass grubs had become a problem following the withdrawal of DDT, was the work of R F Markey; later laboratory and field studies were carried out by D D Evans, C J Hale and Grace Gillard, and trials in Central America and Japan were arranged by P Rivett.

Development work in USA, Japan and the UK showed that seed dressings were the most efficient method of application against bean seed fly *(Hylemyia cilicrura)* on cucumbers, peas, beans and groundnuts. An encapsulated formulation which incorporated a fungicide gave particularly good results in the UK at a time when the demise of dieldrin had made a satisfactory replacement vitally necessary. A very similar problem was that of onion fly *(Hylemyia antiqua)*, where there was also a need for a dieldrin replacement and, in both the UK and Poland, seed dressings gave excellent results and were adopted commercially.

In both cases, the effectiveness of seed treatments depends on the product remaining where it is put, and not being too readily taken up by the growing plant or leached away to the soil. Subsequent work showed pirimiphos-ethyl to be relatively immobile in the soil, and this, combined with its lack of penetration into plants, clearly contributed to its effectiveness. Conversely, where the desired site of action was beneath the soil, leaching down proved to be inadequate and placement at the required level was found to be necessary. This was the case for control of carrot fly *(Psila rosae)* in the UK and France, where trials showed that incorporation in the seed bed or in the row with the seed was essential. With cabbage root fly *(Hylemyia brassicae)*, it was demonstrated that accurate application of granules closely round the collar of the plant gave better results than a band application, while work in Poland with dips, drenches and granules mixed into soil blocks all gave excellent results. Similarly, incorporation of granules into the casing soil of mushroom beds to control Sciarid flies, work conducted jointly by Plant Protection Ltd and the Glasshouse Crops Research Institute, was entirely successful; one essential ingredient of this success was the non-fungitoxicity of pirimiphos-ethyl.

Immobility in soil, elsewhere a virtue, was thought to be the reason for the compound's inadequacy against the important soil pests wheat bulb fly *(Leptohylemia coarctata)* and wireworm *(Agriotes* spp.*)*, and, whilst work by co-operators in Tanzania demonstrated high activity against the Scarabaeid *Cochliotis melolonthoides* on sugar-cane when granules were incorporated on planting the setts, attempts to develop pirimiphos-ethyl for control of the more notorious Scarabaeid *Costelytra zealandica,* (the New Zealand grass grub), proved less satisfactory because incorporation was impossible and the efficacy of surface application was limited by the slowness of downward leaching in comparison with, say, fensulphothion. The same problem may have militated against more than partial success in United States work on *Popillia japonica* and the other chafers in turf, but the persistence of pirimiphos-ethyl on the soil surface was responsible for good results on webworms *(Herpotogramma* spp.*)* and chinch bugs *(Blissus* spp.*)*.

Pirimiphos-ethyl has made an important contribution to the control of the banana weevil *(Cosmopolites sordidus)*. In Ecuador and elsewhere in Latin America, aldrin had for long been used, but strains of weevils appeared which were resistant to all organochlorines, and alternatives had to be found among the organophosphorus compounds. Fensulphothion was effective but highly toxic, and a safer compound was required. Pirimiphos-ethyl was much safer and proved to be highly effective, persisting for six months or more on the soil surface around the mat under tropical rainfall, and killing adults as they attempted to oviposit in the base of the pseudo-stem [4].

In a different sphere, that of veterinary entomology, recent trials in Uruguay and Argentina have shown pirimiphos-ethyl to be effective on (OP susceptible) cattle ticks and sheep mange mite and surprisingly persistent in muddy water.

Pirimicarb

Although the 1950s and early 1960s represented the hey-day of discoveries in the organophosphorus insecticide field, pesticide chemists throughout the world were also 'hedging their bets' by looking for alternatives to organophosphorus compounds. Claims in the patent literature that certain heterocycles containing an enolisable carbonyl group, e.g. pyrazolinones and pyrimidinones, had been phosphorylated and carbamoylated to give compounds having insecticidal activity, led R Ghosh and N D Bishop at Jealott's Hill to investigate the carbamoylation of such heterocycles bearing basic substituents. There were, as it happened, large numbers of pyrimidinones (hydroxypyrimidines) suitable for carbamoylation available at Jealott's Hill, as a result of the parallel investigations which led to the discovery of pirimiphos-methyl and pirimiphos-ethyl.

The first pyrimidine carbamate made and submitted for testing in March 1965 showed insecticidal activity, and this was soon followed by more than fifty compounds represented by the general formula shown in **IV**, page 102. Although many of these compounds were moderately active against several orders of insects, the outstanding feature of the group as a whole was the very rapid kill of aphids. The rate of knock-down and kill at very low rates was quite spectacular, and structure-activity studies were designed to optimise this property.

The compounds which eventually emerged as the best were those of **IV** in which R^1 to R^6 were lower alkyl groups, particularly methyl or ethyl groups, although R^4 could be anything from methyl to hexyl.

An interesting discovery was that the compounds with C_3 to C_5 n-alkyl substitution at R^4 showed a combination of insecticidal and fungicidal properties, and for a while it was considered that such a compound might be developed for the dual control of aphids and mildew, for example on glasshouse ornamentals such as chrysanthemums. In the event, it was decided that it would be more advantageous to develop the best aphicide and the compound now known as pirimicarb, in which $R^4=CH_3$ (**V**, page 102), was selected, having regard to intrinsic activity, mammalian toxicity and ease and cost of manufacture.

Further synthetic effort in this area continued for some years. One compound which was made and found to be almost as effective as pirimicarb itself was the 2-methylamino analogue. The high level of activity of this compound was not unexpected and it was subsequently shown by D J W Bullock that it was a primary metabolite of pirimicarb in plant tissue and presumably contributed to the insecticidal activity of pirimicarb.

Evaluation and Development

In selecting pirimicarb as the most promising of the group, Baranyovits and Joan Masters had in mind a number of characteristics that, ideally, an aphicide should possess; these were derived from a study of existing products, notably ICI's own menazon and Bayer's demeton-methyl. Aphids frequently infest parts of the plant that are not easily covered by an insecticide spray; thus, they are found in the hearts of lettuce, and on the lower leaves in the dense canopy of a potato crop. To kill them in such situations a chemical needs to move from the leaf surfaces which catch the spray to the location of the pest. This it can do either by entering the system which the plant uses to transport sugars and other products of photosynthesis (the phloem), by uptake from the soil and transport in the transpiration stream (in xylem vessels) or, in the case of volatile chemicals, by diffusion through the surrounding air.

Pirimicarb's fumigant effect was demonstrated by inverting a glass beaker, the inner surface of which carried a deposit of the chemical, over a broad bean infested with the pea aphid, *Macrosiphum pisum,* in such a way that none of the leaves touched the glass. Aphids began to fall from the plant within 20 minutes, and after 2 hours all were dead. When a radioactive sample of the product was employed, it could be detected readily in both the aphids and the broad bean.

Evidence for the movement of chemical within the plant was sought in other experiments. In one line of work, droplets of pirimicarb solution were placed on a leaf with a syringe, while aphids were placed on other leaves. When a fan blew air over the plant to prevent the build-up of a lethal concentration of vapour, the aphids remained unaffected, indicating the inability of the chemical to move within the plant from one leaf to another. A similar experiment, in which droplets were placed on the upper leaf surface, while aphids were caged on the lower surface, demonstrated the chemical's ability to move across the leaf, a useful property since natural infestations are often found on the undersides of leaves, and because infested leaves sometimes roll up tightly, enclosing the insects so that spray droplets cannot reach them directly.

Although pirimicarb cannot move from leaf to leaf, it was easy to show that it was transported readily from roots to leaves and this opened up the possibility of using soil-incorporated granules or drenches in suitable circumstances. Applied experimentally in this way, the compound kept broad beans free of aphids for up to three months. Spray deposits on the leaves, on the other hand, tended to have a short life, of the order of a few days only.

Early field experiments were carried out in Italy where, in the peach orchards of the Po valley, aphids (Myzus persicae), through long exposure to a variety of organophosphorus insecticides, had developed multiple resistance. Under these extreme circumstances, pirimicarb sprayed at high volume gave rapid and effective control.

In 1967 and 1968, Baranyovits, Markey, Joan Masters and Mees undertook extensive experiments in the peach growing areas of Italy, France and Spain, the undoubted success of which owed much to the help received from members of the associated ICI companies in the countries concerned; J F Roques and L Paté in France, G Paulin in Italy, and A Martinez in Spain.

A concentration of 0·25% pirimicarb sprayed at high volume with an efficient machine was found to give excellent control, replacing several applications of less effective products. This rate of use was both economic and attractive to the farmers in whose orchards the experiments were carried out because of the particularly rapid aphid kill.

Pirimicarb residues on the fruit presented no problem because the compound was so volatile that little remained on the crop, any that did being rapidly degraded in sunlight.

The peach aphid market alone, however, though locally lucrative, would never have justified development of such a specific product. Baranyovits insisted that organophosphorus aphicides would become less and less effective, partly due to increasing aphid resistance, and partly because, as application rates of such compounds had to be increased to give adequate control, aphid parasites and predators would increasingly be eliminated, and this syndrome was likely to be repeated in other crops [5].

Plant Protection began selling pirimicarb for use on peaches in 1969, whilst other uses were presaged by field trials already in progress on sugar beet in England, Germany, Spain and Holland, on potatoes and on a variety of vegetable crops.

A market on chrysanthemums arose rapidly because some popular varieties were often unsaleable as a result of the presence of aphids that could not be killed by the products then available. A smoke formulation of pirimicarb, developed in Holland, provided a very convenient and labour saving way to apply the product in glasshouses, where it is now widely used on food crops such as lettuces and capsicums.

Work at Jealott's Hill by Margaret Chandler and R T Taylor led to the development of the 'Rapid' aerosol for use in small gardens, whilst, for larger scale use, formulation as a dispersible granule ('Aphox') made the measuring of orchard and field-scale quantities easier and more pleasant.

Aphid resistance to organophosphorus compounds has developed during the 1970s as predicted, to the extent that many such materials are no longer recommended for use on certain crops. The concept of integrated control of pests, which advocates the restrained use of specific pesticides to assist natural control agents, has steadily gained ground and pirimicarb today is widely recognised as being uniquely suited to integrated-control programmes.

An example of such a programme is that developed by N W Hussey and co-workers at the Glasshouse Crops Research Institute in the UK, in which populations of the glasshouse red spider mite and whiteflies are 'managed' or controlled by the introduction to the crop of, respectively, the predatory mite *Phytoseiulus persimilis* and the Chalcid *Encarsia formosa*. The use of pirimicarb on such crops enables aphids to be controlled without harming either predator [6].

A major use which was not foreseen however, has arisen as a result of the rapid development in recent years of aphids as pests of cereal crops. In June 1974, an FAO working party set up an International Project to study the damage due to cereal aphids in Europe, and pirimicarb was selected as the preferred aphicide for the study because of its efficacy and safety; in 1976, which saw an unprecedentedly severe attack of aphids on cereals, pirimicarb was used on approximately 1 million acres of crops in the UK alone. In 1975, 'Pirimor', another of the commercial names under which pirimicarb is sold, was awarded a Gold Medal for product excellence at the 68th Budapest Agricultural Fair, and in 1977 it gained for ICI Plant Protection Division the Queen's Award for Technological Achievement.

References

[1] Anon (1976) '"Actellic"—a broad spectrum pesticide for agriculture and public health' *Int. Pest Control* **18** (1) 4

[2] McCallum Deighton J (1976) '"Actellic" for use against public health insect pests' Insectic. & Fungic. Symposium, Kiev, March 1976. Reprints from: ICI Plant Protection Division, Fernhurst, Haslemere, Surrey, UK

[3] McCallum Deighton J (1978) 'Stored produce insects and their control *Outl. Agric.* **9** (5) (in press)

[4] Pullen J (1973) 'The control of the banana weevil *(Cosmopolites sordidus)* in Latin America and the Caribbean with pirimiphos-ethyl' *PANS* **19** (2) 178–81

[5] Baranyovits F L (1973) 'The increasing problem of aphids in agriculture and horticulture' *Outl. Agric.* **7** (3) 102–8

[6] Binns E S (1971) 'The toxicity of some soil-applied systemic insecticides to *Aphis gossypii* (Hom: Aphididae) and *Phytoseiulus persimilis* (Acarina: Phytoseiidae) in cucumbers' *Ann. appl. Biol.* **67**, 211–22

Chapter 12

Involvement overseas

Initially the overseas extension of Jealott's Hill's activities was related to specific product opportunities, with particular territorial emphasis on commonwealth and colonial countries—where the principal ICI overseas companies were located, or where relations were established with agricultural administrators and scientists of the Colonial Service.

Such activities resulted in a number of noteworthy contributions to the control of major pests and diseases, including citrus scale *(Aonidiella aurantii)* with cyanide fumigation in Palestine; desert locust *(Schistocerca gregaria)* with BHC 'Agrocide' products in the Middle East and Africa; cotton blackarm disease *(Xanthomonas malvacearum)* with the organo-mercurial 'Agrosan' and the copper fungicide 'Perecot' in Africa; and tea blister blight *(Exobasidium vexans)* with 'Perenox' in India and Ceylon (now Sri Lanka).

In the autumn of 1948 B A (later Sir Bernard) Keen, head of the East Africa Agricultural and Forestry Research Organisation (EAAFRO) asked W V Blewett of Central Agricultural Control for ICI's help in solving the problem of bacterial blight of cotton, or "blackarm" as it was commonly called in Uganda.

G Watts Padwick, then recently returned from India, took charge of investigations and, from re-examination of Uganda Department of Agriculture research files, decided to concentrate on the treatment of seed with cuprous oxide using, because of the nature of the disease in Uganda, plots of one square mile in extent.

W T Cowan at Fernhurst and, later, I Mitchelson at Jealott's Hill supervised the field experiments, while R V Tipler and I W Callan at Hawthorndale carried out supportive tests using petri-dish techniques in which, at first, cuprous oxide failed to show any inhibition of the bacterial pathogen; but when live cotton seeds treated with the test chemicals were placed in the nutrient agar dishes, which were then seeded with bacteria, the looked-for sterile zone appeared. [1]

As a result of this work the Uganda Government adopted the cuprous oxide seed treatment (under the name 'Perecot') making its use compulsory throughout the country. Plant Protection Ltd helped in developing the seed-treating machinery, at first by adapting large-scale batch treaters used in the UK for mixing feedingstuffs, but later by developing continuous-feed treating machines (described in an earlier chapter). The treatment was adopted in Kenya, Tanganyika (now Tanzania) and eventually in Nigeria (where 'Agrosan' was used). For the next eighteen years either ICI or PPL kept a technical officer in Uganda working with the government on cotton or other plant protection problems; it was a pattern of research, technical and commercial co-operation which paved the way for similar commitment in other countries.

In 1953, the Gold Coast (now Ghana) and Nigeria Departments of Agriculture, and the West African Cocoa Research Institute (WACRI) commenced field trials with insecticides and fungicides for the control of two of the major problems of the cocoa crop—the capsid bugs, *Sahlbergella singularis* and *Distantiella theobroma,* and black pod disease, *Phytophthora palmivora*; and effective treatments began to emerge from these trials. There were major problems to be solved, however, in the choice of application methods and equipment suitable for the farming systems of the two countries. Through contacts with officials in the Colonial Service, ICI, Plant Protection's advice and participation in finding solutions to these problems were invited. Thus started a close association with the West African cocoa crop which has continued to this day. Plant Protection contributed staff (notably I J Balls, A Bloomfield and D A Harris) and know-how, particularly in the selection of sprayers and their testing under field conditions, arranging modifications with manufacturers, and eventually helping to set up supply and servicing facilities and to train operators and farmers in the use and maintenance of equipment. On the biological side ICI/PP scientists at various times collaborated with or assisted WACRI and the Departments of Agriculture in the selection and refinement of appropriate insecticide and fungicide regimes—notably the gamma-BHC product 'Gammalin' 20 (known as 'PP Kumakate' in Ghana) for capsid control [2], and the copper fungicide 'Perenox' for blackpod [3]. Of the many people involved, perhaps J H Stapley and I E Darter should be singled out for their lengthy involvement in Ghana and Nigeria respectively. The successful introduction of these techniques had a profound improving effect upon cocoa yields in the two countries—one estimate is that in the late-1960s increased production worth $66–132m was obtained for an expenditure of about $6m on pesticides [4].

Overseas Development Department

In the early-1960s ICI's crop protection scientists faced their greatest challenge—to turn paraquat from an intriguing novelty into a major profit-earner for ICI—which, in effect, meant proving its agricultural usefulness.

Since it was clear that production would need to be on a substantial scale before the product cost could be anywhere near a level that would justify agricultural use, this meant, of necessity, an exhaustive and imaginative examination of its potential, world-wide.

Certain prospective uses for paraquat were easily identified—for example, as a replacement for sodium arsenite and sodium chlorate in weed control in rubber and oil palm plantations in countries like Malaya. But W R Boon, J F H Cronshey and S H Crowdy at Jealott's Hill visualised many potential uses for paraquat where weedkillers had never been used before—or if they had, they were of the soil-acting persistent type. These uses lay in the area of "minimum cultivation" and "ploughless farming", such as those which the Jealott's Hill workers were beginning to explore in their trials on direct seeding of a wide range of arable crops into paraquat-killed pasture sward on the Jealott's Hill farm, and on direct re-seeding of mountain pasture in North Wales.

It became clear to Boon that the conventional method of developing a new pesticide in overseas countries—by placing samples and data sheets with key workers in research stations and universities—would not realise the full potential that he visualised for paraquat, because most official workers would be inclined to make the compound fit their testing systems, rather than be prepared to design new systems of farming around paraquat. Additionally, field experimentation would, in many cases, involve several years' rotation of crops and, because of the need to compare conventional cultivation techniques with the new ideas, trial plots would have to be big and would need to be taken through to yield. This amounted to a greater commitment of time and resources than could reasonably be expected of most co-operators. Boon persuaded his fellow directors of Plant Protection Limited and members of the ICI Board that investment in a *corps* of field experiment teams around the world was as necessary as investment in manufacturing plant. The magnitude of such a change in PPL's research resources and expenditure was unprecedented.

The first outline plan indicated a need for about 40 graduates and over 100 total staff dispersed over all continents. This was to carry out, not demonstrations or simple short-term experiments but the longer-term work necessary to assess the true value of new uses for paraquat, and to derive suitable agricultural systems to make the best use of the more revolutionary of them.

The new Overseas Development Department (ODD) was inaugurated in 1964, with the task of identifying and proving potential new outlets for paraquat (and also diquat, other bipyridyls and the aphicide menazon). This was done, wherever possible, in partnership with ICI overseas companies, to ensure their commitment to the research programme and to benefit from their local resources and administration facilities.

Staffing was accomplished by using experienced men from Plant Protection Ltd and the overseas companies, where they could be spared without undue detriment to other activities, and recruiting the rest—almost all staff below technical officer (field team leader) level being local nationals.

For the management of the new department (J F H Cronshey, assisted by I E Darter, E M Godbold and H C Mellor) this involved a hectic period of interviewing, selection and training. It was fortunate that, at the time, a

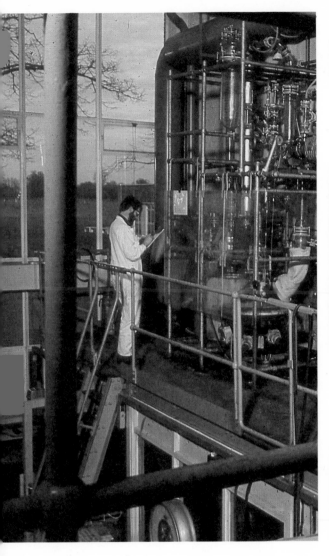

2

1 Large-scale synthetic chemistry
  unit
2 J T Braunholtz

1 I T Kay
2 A Calderbank and J F Newman
3 Adding enzyme substrate to soil
4 Gas chromatography

number of experienced agricultural specialists were becoming available
from a rapidly-contracting Colonial Service, and they provided a strong re-
inforcement to the structure. Fourteen years later, many of the staff who
joined the new department occupy senior positions in Plant Protection
Division and ICI overseas companies.

The principal research programmes embarked upon, and the countries
where they were started were:

Minimal cultivation	Wheat	France, W Germany, Australia, Canada, Argentina
	Maize	France, W Germany, Italy, Canada, S Africa
	Rice	Italy, India, Malaysia
	Vines	France, Italy, S Africa
	Citrus	S Africa
Pasture and fodder crop establishment and management		France, Australia, New Zealand, Canada, Argentina

In addition, co-operative programmes of field experiments in direct-drilling
and minimal cultivation were arranged in East Europe, notably in Hungary,
Czechoslovakia, Romania and Yugoslavia. Plant Protection Limited was
one of the first commercial companies to have a co-operation agreement,
signed in 1966, with the Hungarian State Office for Development and the
Ministry of Agriculture for providing technical advice and setting up
research programmes.

In the USA, where Chevron Chemical Company were undertaking
development work with the bipyridyls, ODD maintained regular liaison
with them and their co-operators.

These field trials were impeccably carried out by any standards and a
great deal of scientifically valuable information was obtained. But the effects
of the programme, judged by the commercial criterion of impact upon sales
of paraquat, were surprisingly varied. 'Spray-seed' is now an acccepted
practice on wheat farms in Australia; fodder crops are direct-drilled in New
Zealand; paraquat features in rice culture in a number of Far Eastern
countries and in vines, citrus and other tree crops around the world. But
direct-drilling of maize has not yet been adopted widely in any of the
countries where these research programmes were undertaken originally. It
is, of course, now increasingly practised in the USA, and in Brazil, where
staff from the original Overseas Development Department are currently
involved in the most dramatic extension of minimum tillage techniques that
has yet been seen—to combat massive soil erosion in the wheat/soya
rotation of Parana and Rio Grande do Sul [5].

The Department was also instrumental in developing crop desiccation
techniques using the bipyridyls, in areas as diverse geographically as

Mexico, Australia and East Europe [6], where bad weather and weed development can hinder harvest; but its influence went far beyond such technical achievement and many overseas ICI Companies that hosted the original teams were stimulated to develop their own organisations, functioning on similar lines to those imported with the ODD teams, but staffed completely by local agronomists. These teams have strengthened the overseas capability of the Company and helped to ensure the vigorous development of new products and ideas, noteworthy among which have been the pyrimidine fungicides and insecticides discovered at Jealott's Hill.

Large-scale Synthetic Chemistry Laboratories 1969

With these newer discoveries, however, fundamental problems concerned with the evaluation of candidate products became apparent, necessitating a different kind of capability, and in 1970/71 the Overseas Development Department, having served its purpose, was disbanded or, more properly, resorbed by the technical departments of Fernhurst and Jealott's Hill.

Field Screening Stations

Escalating costs of pesticide development and an increasing competitiveness in the industry made it essential for Plant Protection to be able to characterise, evaluate and judge the global commercial potential of candidate products in the shortest possible time. This required different facilities from those provided by ODD staff, who were geared to field-scale adaptation of products whose biological and chemical characteristics were already known.

Field screening called for laboratory, glasshouse and field plot facilities to enable detailed work to be done on relatively numerous candidate chemicals and, because the early stages of evaluation of pesticides involved the treatment of crops and soils with chemicals whose toxicology and residual life were incompletely characterised, it was necessary to be able to exercise complete control over the disposal of treated crops, and access to and use of treated soil.

Since 1970, under Research Director J T Braunholtz, and managed by R S Elias, a global network of field stations has been established, appropriately located to enable testing to be carried out in conditions representative of all the major world crop areas. By siting stations in the Northern and Southern hemispheres and in the tropics, each type of test can be carried out in at least two locations at any one time and at least twice in any one year so that the biological properties of chemicals can be assessed correctly and with minimum delay.

The twelve stations at the time of writing are:

Temperate Regions	UK—Berkshire
	France—Haute-Garonne
	USA—Illinois
Warm Temperate	USA—North Carolina
Mediterranean	Spain—Valencia
	USA—California
	Australia—New South Wales
Sub-tropical/Tropical	USA—Florida
	Brazil—Sao Paulo
	India—Mysore
Tropical	Malaysia—Melaka
	Philippines—Luzon

The total area occupied by the field stations is almost 300 ha and they employ some sixty specialist scientists and agronomists, most of whom are locally recruited nationals. The technical staff keep in very close contact with research institutes, agricultural universities and similar organisations in their regions.

The stations provide all the facilities required for the exhaustive testing of chemicals on all the important crops and against the major weeds, pests and diseases. Highly specialised field testing procedures have been developed to ensure that sufficient information on the efficacy, consistency of effect and crop safety of chemicals is obtained to enable reliable recommendations to be made for their use by farmers. Each year up to one hundred potential new crop protection or plant regulating chemicals are tested on the stations; of these about fifteen will be further evaluated, of which ultimately, perhaps one may find a use in agriculture.

Jealott's Hill is the organising centre of this worldwide field testing activity and a continuous flow of visits and technical information takes place between scientists at Jealott's Hill and those in the overseas field stations.

This leads, not only to the rapid development of new products, but also to a better understanding of problems and trends in agriculture and of the present and future role of chemicals in crop protection throughout the world, so that ICI's research can be more closely aligned to the needs of the farming community. The rapidity with which the field stations have been established has borne little resemblance to the normal pace of events in agriculture. To achieve this has required massive effort and extensive use of technology of which the establishment of the 16 ha research farm at Bangalore in India is a good example. Through an unusual but highly successful partnership between the Alkali and Chemical Corporation of India and the Indian army, rock outcrops were blasted and removed, top soil was set to one side, to be replaced after levelling had been carried out; roads were constructed and drains and culverts were made using the blasted rock. This whole process was completed in four months and within another four months the research farm had been surveyed and fertilised, provided with offices, laboratories and services and planted with a large and varied range of plantation, field and garden crops and a collection of the major weeds. During this period of time the Indian staff were given initial training, and 27 trials had begun with insecticides, herbicides, fungicides, viricides and growth regulators. In common with the other field stations a full year's trials programme will involve over 100 field experiments. One of the last to be commissioned, this station was formally opened in November 1976, when government officials, agricultural scientists, administrators and farmers were invited to see the experimental work then in progress.

During the seven years the field station network has been in existence, the farms have suffered tornadoes, hailstorms, floods, droughts, freak frosts and the depradations of marauding animals. Despite these and other constraints the research farms carry out each year over 1000 trials on all the major world crops, pests, diseases and weeds.

To help the station network to function as a unit and to make use of the very considerable technical expertise of the staff, an International Conference is held at Jealott's Hill each year to discuss results and to exchange ideas and information on agronomy, pest control, application, safety and related subjects.

In addition to the annual conference, day-to-day contact is essential to the smooth working of the research programmes, and particularly to ensure that information gained in one station is made available for the benefit of others. This is the responsibility of the overseas field screening Co-ordinator, a role initially played by A R Crossman and currently by R E Plowman. Their main job has been to ensure a steady flow of experimental compounds, equipment and technical information between Jealott's Hill and the field stations. This flow has sometimes been far from steady as the global network emerged from ideas into reality. The field stations are always hungry for chemicals, equipment, technical information and expertise, most of which have had to be supplied from Jealott's Hill.

The biologists are keen to test their latest, most active compound in the field, which has always meant increasingly intensive activity as the last date for shipment approaches. It may take up to three months to synthesise a sample for field testing. A certain amount of process work must be done as it is not always possible to convert the laboratory-scale preparation of 1 gram to a field trials amount of 1 kilo simply by proportionally increasing the ingredients. Starting materials which can be readily purchased in small quantities are often unobtainable in larger amounts which means that the starting materials themselves may have to be synthesised. And the yield from a first-time reaction is to some extent unpredictable; too little chemical produced could mean the loss of an important trial. Such problems are the concern of the Large-Scale Chemical Synthesis Unit, originally set up under J M Winchester and developed by C Shepherd and D F Charlton. There may be little time for formulation work, yet a fairly sophisticated formulation is needed if a chemical is to perform well in the field and, with time running out, this tests the skill and experience of the formulation chemists such as D Day, J C Lawrence, G J Marrs and R P Warrington. All field testing samples are airfreighted by direct airline. However, each sample on its journey will be handled by at least two agents and cargo personnel of the airlines. There are complex regulations governing the packaging, labelling and importation of experimental chemicals. A pilot can, rightly, refuse any package entering his aircraft. With such constraints, there is no room for error. A relatively small delay could defer by six months vital information on the performance of a chemical in the field. The production and shipment of chemicals is, in itself, an art which has been refined so that few mistakes now occur. Even though the chemicals arrive safely and in time, however, field trials are at risk from other factors—such as weather.

A freak hailstorm devastated the Illinois field station, flattening crops, and ruining valuable herbicide and plant growth regulator trials in the space of an hour. Totally unexpected frosts in Brazil in 1975 destroyed or damaged coffee and banana plantations, and snow fell at the Florida station during the winter of 1976/77 for the first time in history. Floods in Australia meant taking a 200-mile diversion to reach the field station at Griffith.

As well as weather, pests and diseases can be unpredictable. In certain cases, such as vine downy mildew (one of the most important European fungus diseases), the use of a misting system can always ensure a good infection at the French field station near Toulouse. However, natural infections and infestations are used for most diseases and pests; the stations were deliberately situated in areas where diseases and pests reliably occur in a typical year but, as all farmers know, there is no such thing as a typical year; as a form of insurance, replicate experiments are carried out on the same target at one or more of the other field stations in the appropriate season, thus ensuring that good reliable field results will be obtained with all possible speed.

Good communications and prompt reporting of results are vital for the network because of the great distances between the field stations. Interstation discussion of methods and techniques is encouraged although most communication is channelled through Jealott's Hill. Every station has a telex facility and frequent use is made of the telephone. A very sophisticated facsimile-copier link has been installed between Jealott's Hill and Goldsboro, the Biological Research Centre of Agricultural Chemicals Division of ICI America, which co-ordinates the activities of the four field stations in the United States.

Communications have not always been so sophisticated. The rather heavy use of punctuation in early reports received from the field station in Brazil aroused some speculation: on enquiry it proved to be the nocturnal contribution of a bat (species undetermined) which co-tenanted the somewhat primitive office facilities!

References

[1] Tipler R V (1953) 'Some experiments on the control of cotton blackarm disease *(Xanthomonas malvacearum)* EFS (Dowson) by chemical seed treatments' *Proc. 3rd int. Congr. Pl. Prot.* Paris 1952, **2,** 655–663

[2] Stapley J H, Hammond P S (1959) 'Large-scale trials with insecticides against capsids on cocoa in Ghana'. *Emp. J. exp. Agric.* **27,** 343–353

[3] Crowdy S H, Elias R S (1956) 'Cacao diseases' *Outl. Agric.* **1,** 64–69

[4] Anon. (1972) *Pesticides in the modern world. A symposium prepared by members of the Co-operative Programme of Agro-Allied Industries with FAO and other United Nations Organisations.* Newgate Press, Ltd. London, 60pp.

[5] Barker M R, Wünsche W A (1977) *'Plantio direto* in Rio Grande do Sul, Brasil' *Outl. Agric.* **9,** 114–120

[6] Sanderson J F (1976) 'Pre-harvest desiccation of oil-seed crops' *Outl. Agric.* **9,** 21–25

Chapter 13

Environmental studies

Contrary to popular misconception, man's awareness of the sometimes fragile nature of his environment did not suddenly burgeon, like flowers in the desert, with the publication in 1962 of Rachel Carson's book *Silent Spring*. It is possible, however, that Miss Carson's book led, directly or indirectly, to much of the mandatory legislation surrounding the present-day use of crop protection products, and not only in the USA.

In Britain, the first official recognition of the need for some control over the use of agricultural chemicals was evidenced by the setting-up of a working party under the chairmanship of Sir Solly Zuckerman to enquire into the safety of workers handling toxic chemicals, the possible risks from the use of pesticides in agriculture, and the possible risks to the flora and fauna.

The first report of the working party led to the passage of the Agriculture (Poisonous Substances) Act 1952 which called for a voluntary Notifications Scheme. Under this scheme, Industry agreed to put no chemical onto the market unless it was safe or, under the conditions of use, created no undue hazard either to users, to consumers of treated crops or to wild life. The scheme was devised, tried for two years and formally introduced in 1957. By the early 1960s, it was clear that it needed an overhaul and, on the initiative of Industry, revision began. This resulted in the development of the Pesticide Safety Precautions Scheme (PSPS) which was introduced in 1964 and is still in effect. Under this scheme, Industry is asked to demonstrate the safety of new pesticides and a programme of work is drawn up in a consultative manner between Industry and Government.

Other chapters of this book illustrate how, well in advance even of voluntary legislation, awareness of potential dangers had led ICI in the 1940s to the preferment of phenyl mercury to the more toxic alkyl mercury compounds as seed dressings, the abandonment of bird narcotics because of possible misuse, and the development of the more costly but less taint-productive gamma-BHC; and in the early 1950s to the extremely rapid jettisoning of the acaricide amiton because of low blood-cholinesterase counts in some spray operators.

Of course these decisions were not altruistic sacrifices; it was recognised early that a high degree of responsibility was essential for the good reputation of the Company. In ICI's agricultural enterprise the various aspects of what is now known collectively as Environmental Science—toxicology, ecology, metabolic studies and residue analysis, like Topsy, 'just growed'. They grew from the need to know why some compounds were biologically active and others not, what happened to a chemical on or in a plant, what was its effect on other organisms and what its fate in soil or water.

So they grew in a rather fragmented way in various parts of the Company in response to developing needs. Studies related to the safety of pesticides were started by Plant Protection in the early 1950s, supported by ICI's Industrial Hygiene Research Laboratories at Welwyn which, on a later move, became the Central Toxicology Laboratories at Alderley Park, near Manchester. Studies on the movement and effect of fertilizers in soil began at Jealott's Hill in the mid-1950s, as did metabolic investigations into the fate of pesticides, by the Chemical Group which had newly arrived at Jealott's Hill; at much the same time residue analysis work commenced at Yalding. The early 1960s saw the beginning of ecological studies in the Biological Group at Jealott's Hill.

The extent and complexity of such work grew rapidly within ICI during the 1960s whilst public and official concern for the environmental implications of pesticide, and particularly insecticide, use was also growing, with the recognition of the harmful long-term effects of a number of organo-chlorine compounds, as exemplified by the population decline in certain species of fish-eating and raptorial birds.

In 1969 ICI Plant Protection Ltd took the far-sighted decision to bring together all its environmental studies by the formation of an Environmental Sciences Group at Jealott's Hill. Three years later the wisdom of this move was seen when the amendment of the US Federal, Insecticide, Fungicide and Rodenticide Act in 1972 enabled the United States Environmental Protection Agency (EPA) to regulate the registration of pesticides in the USA and, by issuing a series of demanding Guidelines, to dictate a standard subsequently followed in principle by the registration authorities of many other major pesticide user countries.

Whilst such legislation increased considerably the cost of developing new crop protection chemicals, ICI, then on the verge of entering the US market through its newly-formed subsidiary ICI (US), was already well equipped to comply with the new regulations.

Today, the Environmental Sciences group at Jealott's Hill employs around 100 people, supported by as many again at the Central Toxicology Laboratories at Alderley Park and by facilities for fish studies at the Marine Biology Laboratories at Brixham.

Ecology

Interest in the environmental impact of new pesticides arose naturally at Jealott's Hill among the entomologists—not because entomologists are endowed with a particular perceptiveness or an inherent social conscience, but because the use of insecticidal treatments traditionally had to take account of bee-keeping interests, because the beneficial effects of predatory and parasitic insects had long been accepted, and because the, by now, widespread concern regarding the use of pesticides had come about as a result of the injudicious use of insecticides. J F Newman who, with H S Hopf and later Ann Harlow, had pioneered the Jealott's Hill insect physiology studies into the mode of action of insecticides, set up, in 1963, a unit to study the ecological effects of pesticides. The unit consisted initially of Newman and N W R Crockford, who had been concerned with refinements in insect breeding procedure, after the departure to Imperial College, London of W O Steel, a taxonomic entomologist of some standing, who had, during the years 1945–59, perfected much of the basic insect-rearing technique in use at Jealott's Hill. There was, however, considerable expertise on which to draw, not least that of the naturalists and bee-keepers G H Stock and J Clayton. As there were no official guidelines, the first studies were designed to examine the impact of related chemicals on a representative range of organisms, as far as possible in the sort of field conditions in which exposure to pesticides might take place.

Attention was given to changes in population in the field rather than to laboratory measurements of toxicity, and this involved the development of techniques capable of producing statistically satisfactory data, with a practicable minimum of effort. With popular press accounts of the 'food-chain' effects on birds of organochlorine insecticide seed dressings, it was inevitable that first studies should be on the effects of pesticides in soil. Long-term small-plot sites were established, initially on Broadricks field at Jealott's Hill, and, with assistance from the Soil Zoology department at Rothamsted, work was begun on the improvement of methods for extracting microarthropods from soil.

The differential wetting technique for separating microarthropods from plant débris, originally suggested by G W Heath at Rothamsted, was modified and improved and has since been used in a routine manner to process large numbers of soil core samples, so that statistically meaningful measurements could be made of changes in the species diversity of the soil microarthropod fauna resulting from pesticide application. This technique later proved useful in investigations of the long-term effects in the soil of direct drilling and other reduced cultivation methods which followed the development of the herbicide paraquat.

The extraction of animals from soil, whilst posing interesting problems of technique, is only preliminary to the identification of the catch. The appointment of W Wilkinson in 1964 brought taxonomic expertise to the unit and made possible the preparation of soil fauna 'balance-sheets'.

The development of diquat and paraquat as aquatic herbicides in the 1960s introduced considerable problems of environmental impact in aquatic systems and the Ecology unit undertook laboratory and field investigations in collaboration with Brixham Laboratory and with the Nature Conservancy Monks Wood Experimental Station (now the Institute of Terrestrial Ecology). In the following years, Ecology Section extended its coverage of wild life surveillance and testing to include earthworms and surface dwelling invertebrates such as beetles and spiders; and went on to the study of birds and small mammals, an area in which the Company's expertise has developed significantly since the appointment of an ornithologist, P J Edwards, in 1970.

The methods used in the British Common Bird Census, developed by the British Trust for Ornithology, have been adapted for the measurement of pesticide impact on birds. Such work is particularly related to the use of pesticide seed treatment. Although a seed dressing is an efficient and relatively safe method of pesticide use, seed-eating birds are clearly at particular risk. Breeding bird territories are now mapped for several weeks before treated seed is sown, and then for a similar time after the seed has been sown, so that any effects on territory occupation can be determined.

A further expansion of interest is instanced by the study of the accumulation of pesticides in a modified Metcalf ecotank system. Using this system, the transfer and accumulation of pesticides along a simple food chain are studied and this has led to a greater understanding of possible accumulation problems when a pesticide is used commercially [1].

Such studies as these, in a newly-emerging field of interest, have necessitated close contact with other research organisations concerned with environmental matters. Jealott's Hill has appreciated not only the importance of sound research on the environmental effect of chemicals in order to gain acceptance by registration authorities, but also its responsibility for making credible results available to other interested parties.

Metabolism

An understanding of the metabolic fate of a pesticide is vital, to determine whether it is likely to degrade or persist in the environment or accumulate in living systems. It is also important to understand the significance of any breakdown products derived from the pesticide which may be present in food or in the environment. A knowledge of the metabolic breakdown of the pesticide may also lead to a better understanding of the mode of action of the chemical.

Nowadays the use of radio-labelled material is the accepted method by which to follow the metabolic fate of pesticides in plants, animals or soil; in the case of most organic compounds, ^{14}C is the most frequently used isotope, but the first radio-labelled work at Jealott's Hill was carried out in the mid-1950s by A J Low, who followed the fate of fertilisers in soil using ^{32}P and ^{35}S labelled chemicals.

In the pesticide field ^{14}C-gamma-BHC had been used by F R Bradbury at General Chemicals Division, Widnes who, working in collaboration with J F Newman at Jealott's Hill, followed the penetration and fate of gamma-BHC in insects. Radio-labelling techniques were also used by J C Gage at Welwyn and later by workers at Jealott's Hill to study the mode of action of organophosphates.

In 1959 metabolism studies in an environmental chemistry sense were initiated at Jealott's Hill by A Calderbank in the newly constituted Biochemistry Section. Radio-labelled diquat and menazon were prepared and the breakdown of these compounds in plants and in soil was studied by Clare Morgan and B Turner. Their progress was hampered by the limited counting equipment then available; radioactivity was measured by what is now seen as the primitive method of planchet counting using an open-end-window Geiger-Muller Tube. A little later a single-pot scintillation counter brought about a significant improvement, but it was only when further improvements in instrumentation were made and a refrigerated, 200-pot, three-channel Packard Scintillation Counter was obtained in 1963 that measurement of radioactivity became rapid and convenient.

Despite the limitations in technique available in the late 1950s and early 1960s some excellent results were obtained. Using radio-labelling techniques such as whole plant autoradiography, menazon was shown to translocate from the roots to the foliage in several plant species. In the leaves, menazon was slowly degraded to several metabolites, two of which were identified, by two-dimensional paper chromatography and autoradiography, as the oxygen analogue menazon thiolate and the hydroxymethyl triazine.

In a similar manner, the fate of paraquat on plants was studied by P Slade who showed that, on the leaf surface in sunlight, the herbicide was degraded to quaternary methyl isonicotinic acid and methylamine hydrochloride [2].

A E Smith studied the photodegradation of diquat in aqueous solution irradiated with sunlight or UV light. The major degradation product was identified as 1,2,3,4-tetrahydro-1-oxo-2H-pyrido [1,2-a] 5-pyrazinium ion (TOPPS) [3].

In addition, several other minor degradation products were identified by co-chromatography, reverse isotope dilution analysis and mass spectrometry.

On plant surfaces diquat also degraded in sunlight. Some volatile products appeared to be formed but identification of other products was hampered by problems of extractability, the presence of plant extractives and the complexity of the degradation. However TOPPS was again identified as one of the products.

After the bipyridyls, in the late 1960s came work on the pyrimidine fungicides and insecticides. Dimethirimol and ethirimol were shown to be metabolised by similar routes; their metabolites, identified by R J Hemingway, B D Cavell and G Teal, varied from simple dealkylated products to glucosides and novel ring-rearranged compounds [4]. At about the same time, studies of the metabolism of pirimicarb, pirimiphos-ethyl, pirimiphos-methyl and, a little later, bupirimate were begun. Some of this work, involving more complex problems, is still continuing.

The need to know what happens to pesticides under field conditions does not stop at plants and soil. Calderbank and others had followed the fate of the bipyridyls in cows as early as the mid-1960s but, by 1971, with the increasing stringency of registration requirements in general and with the proposed registration of bipyridyl applications to crops used for animal food-stuffs, it became clear that additional animal studies would be needed.

This was made possible by the establishment, by J P Leahey and R J Hemingway at Jealott's Hill, of a unit whose concern was the metabolism of pesticides in farm animals. Initially, the metabolism and excretion of paraquat and diquat following a single oral dose to sheep, goats and cows was studied and, in cows and goats, minute traces of radioactive residues in the milk were measured and identified [5]. Animal experiments of this type have now become more complex and goats, pigs or hens are dosed for several consecutive days with the radio-labelled pesticides. The 'in-life' part of the study is now normally contracted out but the analysis of samples, to identify metabolites in meat, milk or eggs, is still carried out at Jealott's Hill. During 1976, a series of additional paraquat feeding studies to identify residues in meat, milk and eggs was carried out by Leahey and P Hendley in goats, pigs and hens for additional registrations in the United States.

Techniques for identifying traces of unknown residues have advanced rapidly. The traditional method of synthesising a probable metabolite and comparing its chromatographic behaviour with that of a radio-labelled metabolite, coupled with reverse isotope dilution analysis, is still followed but is now increasingly augmented by the use of mass spectrometry. The spectrometer at present employed at Jealott's Hill is sensitive to sub-microgram samples and is more and more frequently providing unequivocal sample identification.

This method required the development of sophisticated clean-up procedures, as a result of which the careful use of thin layer column, and high pressure liquid chromatography also developed rapidly. And the application of gas/liquid chromatography with a radiochemical detector, to monitor the elution pattern of metabolites from the gas chromatograph prior to mass spectrometry, has become increasingly important.

As a result, the metabolism teams now have the experience and capability necessary to tackle the complex and detailed studies which are required for registration of new chemicals and of new uses for existing ones.

Residue Analysis

Nowadays, residue analysis is routinely carried out to measure accurately traces of a chemical or its metabolites remaining on crops or in meat, animal products, soil or water after normal agricultural use of a pesticide. Crop samples are taken from field trials immediately after treatment and then at intervals until normal harvesting. Samples of meat and other animal products are taken from controlled trials in which animals are fed diets containing pesticide residues. These samples are carefully analysed and the results are used to establish the levels which might be expected to occur in practice. From this information and toxicological data, the safety of the product in a particular outlet can be assessed. Samples of soil and water from specially designed trials are also analysed to monitor the fate of the pesticide in the environment.

The development of residue analysis technique has closely paralleled and in many ways brought about the development of highly sophisticated instrumentation, so that, now, minute residues can be detected with certainty, accuracy and speed [6].

In the early 1950s, however, at the time of the Zuckerman working party, little was known about residues present on home produced or imported foodstuffs. Methods of analysis for detecting and determining residues were mainly lacking or inadequate and the toxicological significance of residues was unknown. When a residue analysis team was first established at Yalding, its main interest was the detection of residues of amiton and other organophosphorus compounds and methods of analysis were based on measurement of the inhibition of cholinesterase activity.

By 1959, when the unit was transferred to Jealott's Hill under the direction of M G Ashley, residue detection was based mainly on colorimetric methods with limits of detection in the range 0·1–1·0 ppm.

Dramatic changes were soon to take place. With the development of diquat for potato haulm desiccation, analysis of diquat residues in potatoes was of considerable importance; the limit of detection of the then existing method was about 1·0 ppm. On his return from a meeting in 1958 with the US Food & Drug Administration, however, W R Boon shocked the analytical group with a 'request' that the method should be sensitive to 0·01 ppm—a one-hundred-fold increase in sensitivity. But, by an ingenious use of ion-exchange chromatography, coupled with detection of the green colour produced on reduction to the free radical, the desired increase in sensitivity was eventually achieved by A Calderbank, S H Yuen and Claire Morgan. A similar method based on ion-exchange chromatography coupled with detection of the blue free radical was devised for paraquat and it is noteworthy that, twenty years later, this technique still forms the basis for diquat and paraquat analysis.

Further major advances in residue methodology were perhaps slow to develop at Jealott's Hill because of pre-occupation during the 1960s with paraquat and diquat. But in 1970, with the advent of the pyrimidine-based pesticides, it became necessary to make extensive use of modern gas/liquid chromatography technology. M J Edwards, who had recently joined the analytical team, purchased a gas-chromatograph fitted with what was then a new type of nitrogen-selective detector. After suitable clean-up and methylation of crop samples, residues of ethirimol and dimethirimol were detected with far greater speed, accuracy and sensitivity than had been possible before. Soon, a similar chromatographic technique with a nitrogen-selective detector was devised for pirimicarb. This multiplicity of uses arose, by a happy chance, at a time when major improvements to these detectors were being made. The first detectors employed rubidium bromide crystals which needed frequent cleaning and adjustment but, in 1975, rubidium silicate bead detectors were introduced and these proved to be very stable and sensitive and needed no maintenance. Several instruments with the new detectors were introduced rapidly and the residue analysts at Jealott's Hill, among the first users, quickly acquired an expertise in the application of nitrogen selective detectors equalled by few other comparable laboratories.

Rapid and sensitive analytical methods were also developed by D J W Bullock for pirimiphos-methyl and pyrimiphos-ethyl using a flame photometric detector, and, with recent interest in synthetic pyrethroid insecticides, the use of electron-capture detectors has become increasingly important.

Mass fragmentography, a fairly new application of the multiple-ion mass spectrometer, is at present interesting the Jealott's Hill analysts. This technique, whilst not currently acceptable to all Registration Authorities, is likely to become more so in the next few years. Over the past 7–8 years, the need for well-coordinated residue trials programmes carried out in many countries has become increasingly important. These programmes are planned jointly by marketing regions, residue analysts and registration officers. The number of samples generated is increasing at the rate of some 15% per year and about 7000 samples were received at Jealott's Hill in 1976.

This has called for an improvement in the efficiency and speed of handling at a time when regulatory agencies are demanding highly sensitive and highly reproducible methods. Such a requirement has in part been met by the use of automated injectors on the gas/liquid chromatographs and the use of computing integrators to measure the areas of peaks on gas chromatograph charts. The next stage will be to use a computerised data system to control the automatic injectors and to calculate the residues detected.

Soil Studies

Reference has been made to Low's work on the fate of fertilizers in soil, and to that of Tomlinson and Knight on the interaction of bipyridyls with soil, especially soil colloids.

In parallel with the latter, the degradation of paraquat in soil was studied by B C Baldwin, M J Geoghegan and J R Anderson. A microorganism, *Lipomyces* sp, isolated from soil, was shown to be capable of degrading paraquat in culture but, in soil, the firm binding of paraquat rendered the molecule unavailable for microbial attack. Thus, although chemically the molecule is persistent in soil, binding to colloids makes it biologically unavailable, and absence of uptake into crops from soil has been demonstrated in numerous trials at Jealott's Hill and elsewhere.

Interest in the properties of the bipyridyls in soil led to a regard for the effect of pesticides in general on soil microorganisms and soil processes at an early stage. Geoghegan, Anderson and Kathleen Knight developed techniques for studying the effects of pesticides on soil processes such as respiration and nitrification, and these have been improved and extended in recent years by B G Johnen so that the group now has a degree of expertise and knowledge in this field probably unparalleled in an industrial concern.

Much of the early work relied upon *in vitro* studies using isolates of soil organisms. Over the past few years, interest has moved away from such studies to those carried out on 'intact' soil. Highly sophisticated systems have been developed, largely by I R Hill, so that degradation of radiolabelled pesticides in aerobic and anaerobic soil and in aquatic systems can be studied rapidly and conveniently both in the laboratory and in the field, and this work has recently been extended to follow the nature of bound pesticide residues in soil, an area of almost total lack of knowledge.

Methods for measuring leaching, binding and availability of pesticides in soil have been developed and improved in recent years by D Riley and R S Morrod, and are used to provide data for the registration of new pesticides and the selection of candidate pesticides from evaluation compounds.

Registration and Technical Literature

In 1955, when the trial scheme for registration of pesticides was introduced in the UK, a Registration Officer was appointed at Yalding to deal with the submission of data to the Notification panel. Responsibility for such submissions moved to Jealott's Hill in 1959, and shortly afterwards to Fernhurst, where, in 1963, a Registration and Technical Literature Section (RATLS) was formed under N Wright as part of the Overseas Development Department.

With the growth of Plant Protection Ltd's overseas' interests, this Section expanded but registration requirements became increasingly complex throughout the 1960s, particularly when it was planned to enter the US market. It was necessary to continue close liaison with the business needs of the Company but it was essential also to have closer contact with the Research & Development Sections generating Registration data, and in 1969 RATLS, managed by A W Waitt, was transferred to Research Department and became an important part of Environmental Sciences, though it remained geographically located at Fernhurst.

Over the years it has become imperative to co-ordinate registration studies very strictly to ensure that they comply with the requirements of the Registration Authorities of many different countries, for forgetfulness could mean, at the very least, the loss of a year's patent protection. The use of critical path analysis techniques now ensures that deadlines for the submission of registration documents are met and, on completion of the necessary studies, reports are compiled into a registration package by RATLS and submitted to the Registration Authorities. The technical literature side of RATLS is responsible for the production of labels and leaflets, on whose technical accuracy the reputation of the Company, in the eyes of the user of the product, largely depends.

References

[1] Newman J F (1976) 'Assessment of the environmental impact of pesticides' *Outl. Agric.* 9 (1) 9–15

[2] Slade P (1966) 'Fate of paraquat applied to plants' *Weed Res.* 6, 158–167

[3] Smith A E, Grove J (1969) 'Photochemical degradation of diquat in dilute aqueous solution and on silica gel' *J. agric. Fd Chem.* 17, 609–613

[4] Cavell B D, Hemingway R J, Teal G (1971) 'Some aspects of the metabolism and translocation of the pyrimidine fungicides' *Proc. 6th Br. Insectic. Fungic. Conf.* 2, 431–437

[5] Hemingway R J, Leahey J P (1974) 'Metabolism of paraquat in ruminants' *Proc. 3rd IUPAC int. Congr. Pestic. Chem. Helsinki*

[6] Edwards M J (1975) 'Residues: The determination of nothing in everything' *Proc. 8th Br. Insectic. Fungi. Conf.* 3, 787–792

[7] Calderbank A, Clare Morgan, Yuen S H (1961) 'Determination of diquat residues in potato tubers' *Analyst* 86, 569–579

Environmental Sciences building 1978

Bird population studies

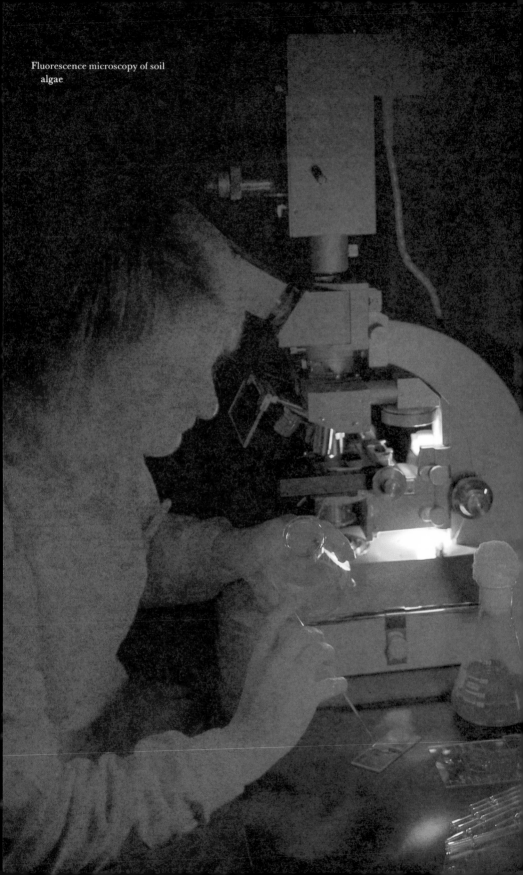

Fluorescence microscopy of soil algae

Chapter 14

'Unsuccessful' ventures

There are those for whom research is the construction, elaboration and testing of a theory, others for whom the orderly marshalling and classification of known facts is a sufficient end, and without them further advance of knowledge would be haphazard indeed. There are innovators and developers—seldom the same people—but so long as there will be a free interchange of scientific thought, ideas will be born, live a little, and either blossom or be re-absorbed. Nature is as profligate with ideas as she is with more tangible forms of life, and the struggle for survival in both is the basis of evolution; nothing is ever lost, nor futile. Genius, however, is bestowed frugally, and the nirvana to which most agricultural research workers aspire is the relative anonymity of association with an idea which comes to practical, and useful, fruition.

To this extent a (not too dismaying) proportion of the research at Jealott's Hill has been 'unsuccessful'. Some was 'before its time'; some was overtaken by time, so that a problem, identified at the outset of the work, had ceased to be important by the time a solution was found; some was academically 'successful' but economically non-viable; very little, as it happened, never got within sight of a solution.

The reader who has progressed thus far will have become aware of the 'blind alleys' associated even with the more 'successful' projects. The present chapter describes further examples of interestings research topics which, in the event, led nowhere but to the general pool of knowledge.

The Improvement of Soil Structure

The beneficial effect of grass in crop rotations was accepted as fact long before anyone saw fit to seek an explanation. Though the effect is partly due to dung and urine deposited by grazing animals, improvement in soil structure brought about by the physical presence and growth of grass roots has been demonstrated [1].

Roots bind soil particles together and produce a 'crumb' structure which facilitates cultivation, improves drainage and, perhaps most important, increases gaseous exchange between the atmosphere and the soil. Experiments at Jealott's Hill and elsewhere have demonstrated increased productivity following one to three year leys, and this has been correlated with improved soil structure. The possibility of artifically inducing this beneficial effect in soils too poor to support a grass crop, by the introduction of soil 'conditioners' such as sodium alginate, had been studied by J H Quastel and D M Webley at Rothamsted, and it was known that various polymeric substances were capable of improving the hydrophilic properties and hence 'crumb' stability of soils.

So also were living organisms, such as bacteria, and products of their metabolism, notably polysaccharides. In 1945, led by a microbiologist M J Geoghegan and supported by a physical chemist, R C Brian, work commenced in a new department at Jealott's Hill to examine the soil-stabilising effect of certain soil microorganisms and the polysaccharides they produced.

Among the organisms cultured by Geoghegan and Brian in order to produce levan and dextran polysaccharides were *Bacillus subtilis* and *Leuconostoc dextranicum*. The bacterial cells and their polysaccharides were incorporated separately into unstructured soils and their aggregating abilities assessed. Cells had little effect on crumb structure but some of the polysaccharides were highly effective.

Several factors contributed to soil structuring activity. In experiments using 0·25% levan, high viscosity was related to high ability for aggregation.

However, viscous solutions of pectin and sodium alginate were not active. Polymers with a nitrogen content exceeding 0·2% were highly aggregating but those with little nitrogen were not.

When the investigations were extended to non-microbial products it was again clear that viscosity was not the only criterion, for in a range of products based on carboxymethyl cellulose, highly viscous solutions were not as effective as the less viscous ones.

Many micro-organisms synthesise lipoids and a number of these were isolated by solvent extraction and tested [2]; extracts of materials as diverse as wheat straw and woodland soils were also tested but they all had low aggregating ability in laboratory tests. At best they were only able to waterproof soil aggregates and so to increase their stability against rain.

Interest in these studies quickened when Monsanto Chemical Co produced the soil conditioning agent 'Krilium'. ICI's Alkali (now Mond) Division requested evaluation of an aniline/furfural polymer which they had manufactured under a code number, RA2484, and which had already successfully stabilised soil against rain for farm roads and field access. With the assistance of E G Bell field trials were carried out in two successive years to ascertain its effect on soil structure and yields of marrow-stem kale. Polyvinyl alcohol and a hydrolysed polyacrylonitrile similar to 'Krilium' were included in the trials.

The overall picture at the end of this time was that, although RA2484 improved the soil structure, the effect was transient and any improvements in growth that occurred were due to nitrogen released from the polymers. The eventual realization that any such chemical would be prohibitively expensive at effective field rates brought the work to an end.

Chlorella

The period 1945–50 saw the beginnings of the current concern over the imbalance of the 'man/food equation' and research workers in several countries were intrigued by the possibility of food production from unconventional sources such as, for example, unicellular green algae. In view of the delicacies made from seaweed for many centuries by the Japanese, food from unicellular algae was not an unreasonable idea, and theoretical considerations led scientists to believe that greater yields per acre were possible than from many traditional crops. Artificially cultured, algae could be maintained in optimum growing conditions whereas field crops are subject to the vagaries of the weather, and the entire yield of material could be utilized whereas, often, only part of a traditional crop is harvested and used for food. Traditional crops make poor use of sunlight during the early period of plant growth development and they 'waste' land in the interval between harvest and sowing the next crop. Such considerations made the culture of algae on a continuous basis very attractive.

The work at Jealott's Hill, which commenced early in the 1950s, was directed by Geoghegan and carried out by Kathleen Knight, P F H Freeman and E G Bell, using *Chlorella vulgaris* as the culture organism. Initially, flasks, aspirators and measuring cylinders were used as culture vessels but as experience was gained in handling bulk nutrient solutions and carbon dioxide gas, and when efficient agitation was introduced, a battery of tubes $4\frac{1}{2}$ feet by $2\frac{3}{4}$ inches in diameter was used. Daylight fluorescent tubes, though expensive to run, gave a constant light source essential when optimising other conditions of culture. Each day, three quarters of the algal 'soup' was run off, the cells were harvested and the filtrate returned to the tubes after suitable adjustment with nutrients and water. Later, a large 'Perspex' tank was set up in a field at Jealott's Hill in which it was possible to culture *Chlorella* under normal daylight conditions. The product was harvested every second day; yields were 0·44 g/l/day using fluorescent tubes and 0·30 g/l/day from the tank in the field.

The cells were obtained as a green paste after centrifuging the 'soup' with a Sharples continuous centrifuge and the paste was then freeze-dried. The dried material was stable for long periods and retained its colour if stored in the dark; it contained about 47% true protein and included the essential aminoacids. It also contained a wide range of vitamins—the ß-carotene content was three times as high as that of good quality dried grass—and it was estimated that 0·25 lb of dried *Chlorella* would provide more than the minimum requirement of all vitamins except vitamin C which, though present in freshly harvested *Chlorella*, decomposed when the product was dried. Feeding tests (other than tastings by unsuspecting visitors to the laboratory) made use of rats at the National Institute for Research in

Dairying. These tests showed that the 'protein efficiency ratio' (grams gain in weight per gram of protein intake), although less than that of skimmed milk, was significantly greater than that of dried brewers' yeast or groundnut meal [3].

However, the calculated cost of developing a mass culture process for algae was too high for it to be used solely to produce food, though economic success could well have attended the use of *Chlorella* as a source of specialist chemicals, e.g. vitamins. As there was little further work that could be carried out on a laboratory scale at Jealott's Hill, the project was discontinued.

Had the fermentation technology recently developed by Agricultural Division at Billingham (the subject of a later chapter) been then available, there may have been a very different outcome to the work.

Soil-less Culture

Plants have been grown without soil for many years as a research technique, to study the effects of different nutrients on plant growth. However, in the late 1930s, mainly as a result of work in the USA, it was suggested that crops could be grown in this way for commercial purposes with advantage, and several techniques were developed.

Templeman and others at Jealott's Hill were amongst those who took up the challenge and in 1939 tomatoes were being grown without soil by an improved technique which required less labour and equipment than most methods in operation at the time. Nutrient solution was fed by gravity to a porous tile drain laid in the bottom of the bed containing a growing medium based on vermiculite. By this means the medium was moistened evenly and the rate of nutrient application could be varied simply by raising or lowering the nutrient solution reservoir. Early work at Jealott's Hill aimed at finding the correct balance and concentration of nutrient ions and comparing the productivity of conventional tomato culture with that of soil-less culture. These experiments and others carried out at a nearby commercial glass-house showed clearly that productivity and the chemical composition of the fruit as measured by N, P_2O_5 and K_2O content were similar for four varieties of tomatoes. Spectrographic analysis showed that there was no difference in the content of sodium, boron, iron and copper.

Radishes, peas, potatoes, turnips and carrots were also grown successfully in the absence of soil with a minimum of disease, as were sweet peas and chrysanthemums, though it was found that, for flower crops, the nitrogen level in the nutrient solution should be varied according to the incident light intensity [4].

It was concluded that fruit, vegetables and flowers grown in sand or vermiculite and fed only with inorganic nutrients were equal to the best that could be grown in soil.

But in 1939, and for the next six years, soil-less culture had to be forgotten in Britain. The factors which might have made it an attractive proposition ceased to exist. 'Artificial' fertilizers were rationed and scarce; labour was plentiful in the shape of the Women's Land Army and innumerable part-time volunteers, and food production was a matter of survival, not commerce.

The expansion of ICI's agricultural interests post-war and its rapidly increasing and successful involvement in crop protection have been described in earlier chapters of this book; though soil-less culture of crops was developing in other countries, notably the USA and Israel, ICI was otherwise engaged.

However, recent developments by A Cooper and others at the Glasshouse Crops Research Institute in Sussex, where many of the earlier disadvantages of soil-less culture have been overcome by constant circulation and aeration of the nutrient, have brought Plant Protection back into this interesting field; not, in this instance, as innovators, but with considerable knowledge of crop nutrient requirements to contribute as co-developers.

Birds as Pests in Agriculture

'Birds as pests' is a concept, for many, difficult to accept. They are 'our feathered friends'; sonnets are written about them, odes to them. Though they may foul public buildings, cause aircraft to fall out of the sky and, in certain parts of the world, descend, in flocks a million and more strong, to ravage already inadequate crops, they are regarded generally with a tolerance and affection accorded to no other competing species.

Farmers even, with the possible exception of fruit-growers, bear them little ill-will; they just wish they would GO AWAY!

Strategies adopted toward this end have been many and varied, and, particularly with the advent of electronic devices, ingenious in the extreme. Birds, however, quickly learn to disregard all but the ultimate deterrent, and the problem remains, a problem.

At Jealott's Hill in the late 1930s many chemicals were tested as seed treatments to find a deterrent against the serious depredations of birds on newly sown agricultural crops. Captive birds were used in these experiments and it was found that when they were very hungry, they readily ate seeds treated with evil-smelling and pungent materials; yet, tasteless substances which slightly altered the feel of the grain, or dyes with unusual colours, were moderately repellent. However, when repellency depended on colour, the effect was only transient.

Later, experiments with a wide range of chemicals supported these findings [5]. In field trials on cereals at Jealott's Hill 'Corvusine', an anthroquinone already in use in certain European countries, was compared with an experimental powder dressing based on 'gas black', a finely-divided form of carbon. 'Corvusine' was markedly repellent to birds but it retarded germination slightly and, if applied in small excess, it made the seed rather sticky. The 'gas black' dressing was initially almost as repellent as 'Corvusine' but the effect did not persist, possibly because its repellency was due to colour only. Moreover, when 'gas black' was experimentally incorporated in the mercurial seed-dressing 'Agrosan' G, fungicidal efficiency of the formulation was depressed. By 1944, several emulsions containing gas tar and pitch had been formulated at Jealott's Hill and, in tests with captive birds, they were consistently more repellent than 'Corvusine' as seed treatments; moreover the treated seed dried more quickly, was less tacky and germinated with only slight delay.

Two of the gas tar/pitch emulsions were tested on oats and barley in nine field trials in 1945. A very early spring in 1945, however, gave birds plenty of alternative food and in only one trial was an attack on the newly sown seed threatened. Even this trial was abortive because, during the period before seedling emergence, the "co-operator" secretly employed a man with a gun to scare the birds away!

An alternative approach met with greater success.

In 1941, a Wood Pigeon *(Columba columbus)* Investigation Unit was set up by the Edward Grey Institute of Ornithology at Oxford to assess the magnitude of the wood pigeon menace and to develop methods of controlling the pest, as part of the war-time effort for increased food production. The wood pigeon had long been known to damage farm crops but although 'shoots' were organised during winter months, they did not effectively reduce the pigeon population. Poisoning was ruled out as undesirable, unselective and a source of danger to other wild life.

As a result of discussions involving R E Slade, ICI Research Controller at the time, and W A Sexton from ICI Dyestuffs Division, work started at Jealott's Hill early in 1942 to discover chemicals which could narcotise pigeons. A selection of these compounds would then be formulated as baits for field-scale testing, mainly by the Wood Pigeon Investigation Unit. It was considered that pigeons accepting the bait should undergo motor-paralysis within about three minutes after the chemical was administered; the effect should last for at least twenty minutes but for not more than two hours and should not give rise to agitation of the bird. The chemical would need to be non-repellent, non-lethal, and have no harmful physiological effects. Narcotised pigeons could than be collected and humanely destroyed while game and harmless birds would be allowed to recover.

Various narcotics and related chemicals were tested by Jameson at Jealott's Hill by administering the dose in a capsule to caged tame pigeons, with the result that 2,2,2-tribromoethanol and 2,2,2-trichloroethanol were selected for field evaluation. Baits were formulated and tested on caged birds and the most effective of these were based on wheat or barley and contained 3–10% of tribromoethanol. Trials were carried out through the winters of 1944 and 1945; the bait was spread evenly over parts of fields which had been sown recently and the number of birds caught was recorded; there were 908 wood pigeons, 348 rooks and 103 stock doves, but only 15 game birds.

The experiments showed clearly that a bait containing a narcotic could be used to capture bird pests on crops [6]. Whilst further studies would have been necessary to produce a commercially acceptable bait, stable on storage and persistent under varied field conditions, there is no doubt that, in terms of finding an answer to the problem, the work was 'successful'; but the sudden realisation of the possibility of creating a new leisured class of scientific poachers led to the decision, no doubt a wise one, just quietly to forget the whole thing.

In 1946, with the return to peace-time mixed farming the wood pigeon threat to cereal growing receded; the birds are still troublesome, particularly to growers of brassica crops, and further work with narcotics has been carried out, notably in the early 1960s by the Ministry of Agriculture's Infestation Control Laboratory in Surrey, but at Jealott's Hill the subject has remained closed.

For any reader who may be nervous of firearms but fond of pigeon pie, a note of caution should be sounded; in Britain, at least, it is illegal to use poison or stupefying baits except under licence.

Control of Plant Nematodes

ICI's involvement with nematodes began in 1949, as the successful development of BHC/organomercurial seed dressings for wireworm control drew to a close. It was then considered, and this may be seen in retrospect as a somewhat parochial assessment, that the potato root eelworm *Globodera (Heterodera) rostochiensis* was the next most important 'entomological' problem to tackle.

Whilst good control of cyst-forming nematodes had been reported following experimental use of a variety of isothiocyanate-generating compounds, interest was largely focused on certain volatile halogenated hydrocarbons, the most commercially successful of which was Shell Chemicals' DD mixture (at that time a rather crude petrochemicals by-product consisting of mixed dichloropropenes and dichloropropanes). By 1951 screening tests at Jealott's Hill (involving an elegant technique never subsequently reported in the literature) had identified a potential product, perchloroethylene 'heavy ends', derived from a General Chemicals Division process for the manufacture of perchloroethylene, and consisting essentially of impure tetrachlorobutadiene. Field trials carried out in the UK in 1952–53 by Jameson, F C Peacock and H C McIlvenny and later, against non-cyst-forming nematodes in West Africa, showed this material to be as effective as DD mixture. It also had the same drawbacks—phytotoxicity, corrosiveness to injection equipment, and an even more disgusting smell, and when a change in the perchloroethylene works process considerably reduced the availability of the by-product, its development potential evaporated. Subsequently, various organic azides, -cyanides, -phosphates and thiocarbanilides, were shown to give good control of nematodes under field conditions, but none approximated to a commercial challenge to existing products.

A new approach to the problem then presented itself. W H Preston & J W Mitchell in the USA had shown that certain compounds, notably α-methoxyphenylacetic acid, were transported from leaf application to, and even out of, the roots of treated plants, and C J Nusbaum had shown that maleic hydrazide not only moved in the same manner but interfered with the development of nematodes in the roots, or antagonised the cellular changes on which such development depended. An aseptic root tissue culture technique was developed at Jealott's Hill by Peacock, J Clayton and Jean Taylor which allowed the effect of chemicals added to the culture medium to be studied, but under these conditions inhibition of nematode development was invariably associated with reduced root growth and there was no way of distinguishing effect on the root from effect on the nematode.

Meanwhile, synthetic chemical effort by J T Braunholtz had produced a novel group of compounds which were shown to move, from application to plant leaves, to the roots, and to inhibit development of root-knot nematodes (*Meloidogyne* spp) provided the nematodes were not already established therein [7]. In field trials in Florida in 1961, however, 1,3,5,tricyanophenyl-pentane—the most promising member of the group—was found to have an insufficient activity/phytotoxicity ratio, and further work was abandoned. Other companies were working along the same lines, and Du Pont's oxamyl, which is effective as a soil treatment, also came close to reaching the goal of a foliar nematicide treatment; but neither the ICI compound nor oxamyl is transported efficiently enough in the plant, heavy and repeated doses being necessary to produce a practically significant effect on the nematodes.

Over the past fifteen years or so various organophosphorus and carba-mate soil-acting nematicides have been developed in the laboratories and testing stations of other chemical companies. Comparable 'success' has thus far eluded the workers at Jealott's Hill.

References

[1] Low A J (1954) 'The study of soil structure in the field and the laboratory' *J. Soil Sci.* **5** (1) 57–74

[2] Geoghegan M J, Brian R C (1948) 'Influence of some bacterial polysaccharides on the binding of soil particles' *Biochem. J.* **43** [1] 5–13

[3] Geoghegan M J (1953) 'Unicellular algae as a source of food' *Discovery* **14**

[4] Templeman W G (1946) 'Sand culture of plants: soil-less cultivation of carnations' British Carnation Society 36–37

[5] Jameson H R (1942) 'Bird repellents—future prospects'. ICI internal Report HLQ 55 (Oct 12, 1942)

[6] Jameson H R (1946) 'The control of bird pests by narcotic baits'. ICI internal Report HLER 48 (Feb 1946)

[7] Peacock F C (1963) 'Systemic inhibition of root-knot eelworm' *(Meloidogyne incognita)* in tomato. *Nematologica* **9**, 581–583

Chapter 15

Single cell protein

The Agricultural Division of ICI, by the mid-1960s, could look back on a record of satisfactory achievement and innovation in heavy chemical engineering technology, particularly in ammonia and fertilizers. In its fertilizer enterprise it had developed a comprehensive and close relationship with the farming business, and its scientific achievement at Jealott's Hill had contributed to the efficiency of that business, particularly in respect of nitrogen fertilizers. However, the advent of steam reforming of naphtha and then natural gas, the introduction of a satisfactory form of fertilizer ammonium nitrate, and the solution of the technical problems of nitrate-based compound fertilizers, had brought technological development to a near plateau. It was time to move on . . .

The Food and Agriculture Group led by P P King searched for alternative potentially profitable ventures for the Division to evaluate. A new Nitrogen Products Section was established under N Watchorn to consider some of these options, with particular emphasis on manufacturing nitrogen-containing products of a higher value than conventional fertilizers. One possibility—that of producing protein-containing animal feedstuffs from fossil fuels, inorganic nitrogen and other salts—had the advantage of strengthening the Division's links with the farming community. The development of fermentation processes to manufacture protein on a scale that would have a significant impact on the animal feeding stuff industry would fully utilise the chemical engineering strength of the Division and would take such processes right out of the scale exhibited, for instance, in antibiotic manufacture.

In the late 1940s an attempt at Jealott's Hill by Geoghegan and others to produce protein economically from unicellular algae had not met with success, but there had been many advances since then in the field of industrial biochemicals. By the late 1960s British Petroleum and several Japanese companies had already developed—to the pilot plant stage—processes for growing protein-rich single cell organisms using long-chain hydrocarbons of petroleum origin as the carbon source. ICI had no captive source of such materials, but at that time natural gas with methane as the major constituent was being extracted from the North Sea deposits, and this seemed to the chemists at Billingham a more suitable starting point. So in 1968 Agricultural Division took its first steps into this new field.

Facilities and many of the staff, particularly for the chemical and chemical engineering aspects of the work, were taken over from the earlier nitrogen fertilizer research activities. However, the Division had no experience of microbiology fermentation processes or biochemistry. D McLennan and J Ousby from Pharmaceuticals Division provided the initial fermentation expertise and T R Owen and A G Turner from the Corporate Laboratory were the first microbiologists to join S R Smith's chemical engineering team at Billingham in 1968.

The initial work concentrated on methane as the carbon source and on finding organisms capable of using it. J R Quayle of Sheffield University joined the team as consultant, advising on the biochemistry of organisms capable of using single carbon molecules. Work was also initiated at the University of Strathclyde under E O Morris and R S Holdom on the various aspects of the fermentation processes. The methane-utilising organisms tested were not particularly promising; their rate of growth was slow and their overall efficiency of carbon utilisation was rather low. Overlying the microbiological problems were the difficulties and safety aspects arising from supplying both methane and oxygen (air) to a very large fermenter.

By early 1969 it seemed more attractive to concentrate work on finding organisms that could use methanol rather than methane. This overcame the safety problems and left conversion of methane to methanol to the chemical process, in which the Division was already a world leader. The decision to use methanol—a water soluble liquid—rather than methane gas simplified the microbiology and the process engineering. The correctness of this decision has been confirmed by subsequent experience. Despite intensive efforts in several countries no economic process for the fermentation of methane has appeared. With methanol, on the other hand, technical progress has been more rapid than with the linear hydrocarbons earlier in the field, and, increasingly, it has come to be regarded as commercially the most attractive basis for single-cell protein manufacture.

The microbiologists at Billingham discovered and isolated several promising methanol organisms from various sources in the years 1969 and 1970; some of them were patented in those countries where this was possible and desirable. Because of the long duration and cost of nutritional and toxicological testing a preferred organism had to be selected at an early stage, and the choice fell on what is now called *Methylophilus methylotrophus*. Subsequent experience has never given a doubt about the wisdom of this choice although of course far less is known about the possible virtues of other methanol organisms.

As the Division's engineering resources were brought to bear on the process design it became apparent that none of the traditional fermenter designs was suitable for the exceptional capacities envisaged for commercial single-cell protein plants. Large stirred vessels give inefficient mixing and high power consumption, and stirrer shafts pose particularly difficult design problems in avoiding the entry of infective organisms. Airlift fermenters, in which circulation through coolers is achieved by the injected air, give poor oxygen absorption efficiencies and, hence, high compression costs.

The problems were solved by F C Roesler at Billingham by a development of the pressure cycle fermenter concept. This involves a fermenter loop in which circulation through a cooler is maintained by injecting air into one side of the loop. The height of the loop (typically 30m or more) is so designed as to give a high enough hydrostatic pressure at the base to ensure the rate of oxygen absorption required by the cells in the fermenter. Free evolution of the carbon dioxide produced is secured by the rapid circulation of the fermenter contents through the lower pressure region at the top of the loop.

ICI PROTEIN PROCESS

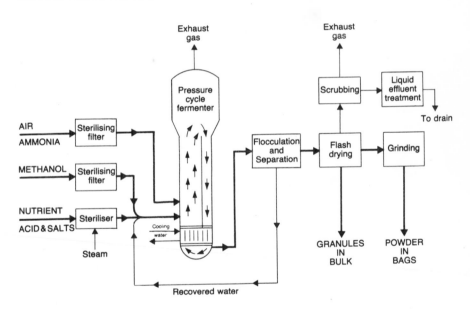

Based on this concept a pressure cycle fermenter was designed in single units for capacities of single-cell protein up to 100,000 tonnes/year or more which would still give a power consumption per tonne of oxygen absorbed, and specific fermenter volume per tonne of oxygen absorbed, well below those of other designs. It was also found possible to adapt the pressure cycle fermenter to other special requirements of the process organism in order to give maximum substrate conversion efficiency.

Laboratory fermenters of about 1 litre capacity were used for the early experiments but the scale of operation was increased step by step and, by early 1971, a continuous fermenter of 1 cubic metre capacity was in use, which was capable of producing tens of tonnes per year. By September 1972 a pilot plant fermenter using the pressure cycle principle was brought into use and, with the attachment of separation and drying equipment, a complete pilot plant to produce some hundreds of tonnes/year was available [1].

Initial testing of the microbial mass obtained from fermenters as a potential protein-rich feedstuff was carried out by D Conning and D Kinch at what is now the ICI Central Toxicology Laboratory (CTL). The results showed the absence of any major safety problem and allowed the scale of operations to be increased from the laboratory to pilot plant scale.

For the first eighteen months the major research activities were carried out at Billingham. In June 1969 Watchorn moved from Billingham to Jealott's Hill where one of his main tasks was to ensure that animal feeding trials and nutritional evaluation kept pace with the increasing availability of product at Billingham. Although Jealott's Hill was experienced in crop production and ruminant nutrition, the main targets for the new protein product were non-ruminants—particularly pigs and poultry—and new facilities and expertise were required. At the end of 1969 the first non-ruminant nutritionist at Jealott's Hill arrived; D A Stringer, who had acquired a reputation particularly in poultry nutrition with British Oil Cake Manufacturers, took the lead role in determining the poultry and pig facilities required for the test programme.

At first the scope of the trials was limited by the output of the relatively small fermenters, and work concentrated on trials with young chicks. In 1971 when a fermenter of 1 cubic metre capacity came into use it became possible to carry out well-replicated comparisons of diets containing single-cell protein with standard commercial diets containing soya bean meal and fishmeal. Such trials involving pigs and broilers soon required more space and staff. Stringer was joined by Diana Smith and other staff, and new animal research facilities were established at Jealott's Hill in what had been an outlying copse known as Wellers Wood. ICI then had the means of carrying out experiments involving up to 150 pigs and 2,000 broilers or laying hens per trial, using small pens and allowing a high degree of replication which was essential for a sensible statistical evaluation of the data.

Later, as confidence in the project grew and promising feeding trial results were obtained, the scale of operations increased. Work on veal calves was added to the pig and poultry work. D G Waterworth joined Stringer at Jealott's Hill and the services were enlisted of consultants such as Tj Bakker who, with the Dutch feed company Denkavit, had many years experience in veal calf nutrition.

It was recognised from the start that, to carry conviction, such trials would be needed not only within ICI but in independent establishments both in the UK and in other countries where it was hoped to sell the product (subsequently named 'Pruteen') or exploit the process. The Jealott's Hill team established a co-operative work programme for the independent evaluation of 'Pruteen' in most of the major potential market countries in the world. In the UK work was carried out at the Universities of Edinburgh and Nottingham, and at the National Institute for Dairy Research; in Holland at the Instituut voor Landbouwkundig Onderzoek van Bio-chemischeproduction; at various National Agricultural Research Centres in France; in Germany at Munich University and the Institut für Kleintierzucht in Celle; and in Japan at the National Scientific Feed Association. This extensive programme not only increased the research capacity but ensured that the product received evaluation in accordance with the specific requirements of these potential market countries [2] [3] [4] [5].

The animal nutrition programme had two main objectives. One was to show the absence of harmful effects from 'Pruteen' either upon animals eating it or upon people eating meat from such animals. The other was to show that 'Pruteen' could be economically incorporated into animal diets under commercial conditions, taking into account likely costs of production and the growth rates and feed conversion ratios shown by animals on diets containing 'Pruteen'.

The first of these aspects involved a close collaboration between the team at Jealott's Hill and the CTL workers in Cheshire. Tissues, organs and body fluids from a selection of the pigs, chickens, laying hens and calves raised on diets containing 'Pruteen' at Jealott's Hill were sent to CTL where they were subjected to detailed examination by D Kinch, A Wilson and their colleagues. Biochemical properties of blood and urine and weights of various internal organs were carefully compared for animals with and without 'Pruteen' in their diets. Microscopic examination of huge numbers of tissue sections were examined and checked for malignant growths or other abnormalities which might be attributed to the new feedingstuff.

Breeding experiments were also carried out at Jealott's Hill on many generations of pigs and poultry in order to establish the absence of effects upon fertility and reproduction and the normality of the offspring, in addition to the more usual testing programme carried through at CTL with rats, mice and other laboratory animals to show absence of toxicity, cancer formations, birth deformities or genetic effects.

The second objective concerned the economics and profitability of the project. A new feedingstuff ingredient must be not only safe, it must be at least equivalent to, and preferably have an advantage over, the ingredients it is intended to replace when price and animal performance are balanced. Pig and poultry feedingstuffs are formulated from a variety of ingredients such as cereals, soya bean meal, fishmeal, and other protein-rich sources, minerals and vitamins, all of which satisfy a detailed diet specification covering metabolisable energy, protein, certain important aminoacids such as lysine and methionine, and many other factors. The objective was to show that, when 'Pruteen' was incorporated into feedingstuffs, with adjustments to other ingredients to meet the specification, animal performance was unchanged in respect, principally, of growth rate and feed conversion efficiency.

This was accomplished with ease but, if this had been all, the ICI protein project would probably have succumbed to unfavourable changes in the economic and political scene that took place in the years 1971–74. However, if the Jealott's Hill work was originally regarded by many at Billingham as an animal testing programme rather than as innovative research, the animal trials then achieved very much more than their original objectives. In order to explain the character of this achievement it is necessary to consider briefly the economics of 'Pruteen' manufacture and use.

Shaping a New Business

In outline, the ICI protein business takes a fuel, namely natural gas, to produce a feedingstuff ingredient which replaces agricultural products in proportions given very roughly by a relation such as the following:

$$1.0 \text{ tonne 'Pruteen'} + 0.3 \text{ tonne cereal} \equiv 1.7 \text{ tonnes soya bean meal}$$

This is a much simplified view of a series of complex relationships involving many more ingredients than those shown and varying somewhat from one particular diet formulation to another (e.g. the relationship for a pig starter diet differs from that for a broiler finisher diet). However the simplified version does give a broadly correct account of the influence of cereal and soya bean meal prices on the value which feedingstuffs compounders would put upon 'Pruteen'. For every £1 increase in the price of soya bean meal the value of 'Pruteen' increased by about £1·7 and for every £ increase in the price of cereals the value of 'Pruteen' decreased by about £0·3.

The cost of manufacture included the cost of the fuel used to make the methanol and to provide the electric power and other materials and utilities taken by the protein plant itself. As a result every £1 increase in the cost of a tonne of fuel increased the cost of manufacture of 'Pruteen' by about £3.

These effects, of world agricultural prices on realisations from sales, and world fuel prices on manufacturing costs, were of crucial importance in determining the economic viability of the ICI protein process. Between the years 1971 and 1975, events in the world at large, acting through these effects, substantially altered for the worse the profit prospects of the ICI protein business.

In 1971 came the agreement on entry of the UK into the European Economic Community, with the prospect that by the time a commercial protein plant could be built, UK cereal and soya prices would be like those in the EEC. Relative to soya prices and also in absolute terms, cereal prices in the EEC had been higher than in the UK. As explained, higher prices for cereals for a fixed soya meal price means a lower value for 'Pruteen'.

The effect of this would have been unwelcome, but not disastrous. Much more important, in 1973 and 1974 the price of fuels increased three- to four-fold. Any attempt to quantify the effect of this is confused by currency inflation effects since 1971 but, expressed in 1976 £s, the activities of the Organisation of Petroleum Exporting Countries in 1973 and 1974 must have added something near £100/tonne to the prospective manufacturing costs of 'Pruteen'.

By 1976 the project had absorbed the heavy adverse impacts of EEC entry and the energy crisis and, even so, it was possible to make a financial justification for a plant of 60,000 tonnes per annum capacity. In September 1976 the ICI Board gave sanction to the expenditure of £40m to construct, on Teesside in NE England, the first commercial plant to make protein from methanol.

The new factors which enabled the project to survive in unfavourable circumstances originated in the Jealott's Hill nutritional studies.

Calf Milk Replacers

Of the two original prospective markets, pigs and poultry, the latter had from the start seemed the more attractive because of the special need of poultry for the sulphur aminoacids of which 'Pruteen' is a rich source. In the less favourable climate of 1972 however it was necessary to look for something better than the pig market.

Salvation was sought in a highly demanding application, namely, as a replacement for skimmed milk powder in calf milk substitutes. Use of such milk substitutes permits diversion of milk to butter manufacture. They are dry mixes of ingredients such as skimmed milk powder, whey powder, fats and starches, which have water added to them for feeding. For veal calves a product low in available iron is required and a dietary ingredient for a veal calf therefore has to meet more stringent requirements than one for a herd replacement animal.

In 1972, work on pigs at Jealott's Hill progressed at a rate that was necessary for the evaluation of the toxicity and teratogenicity work. Resources were increased and switched to an effort to develop a veal calf milk replacer ingredient from 'Pruteen'.

The pilot plant was adapted to the production of a product low in available iron and with good suspension properties in water, and formulation work was started at Jealott's Hill. Because of the high protein content of 'Pruteen' it was possible to replace skimmed milk powder by half its weight of 'Pruteen' plus half its weight of whey powder. With the high price of skimmed milk powder and the low price of whey powder this formulation put a high value on 'Pruteen'.

From an early stage, development work on 'Pruteen' in milk replacers was carried out in collaboration with most of the leading producers and potential customers in Europe [6] [7]. Since then many other investigators in research and commercial establishments have studied the application of 'Pruteen' and the product may now be regarded as well-founded as a satisfactory skimmed-milk powder substitute for animal applications.

When the big oil price rises were taking effect in 1972 a 12-month trial of 'Pruteen' in laying-hen diets was in progress. This conjunction of events led Jealott's Hill experimenters to look at their results very closely for any previously unnoted nutritional virtues in the new product, but nevertheless it appeared providential when a distinct tendency towards higher egg production and improved feed conversion efficiencies was noted for the birds on the experimental diets. Animal feed trials of course have an inherent variability and it was vital therefore to check as quickly as possible whether a real effect had been observed.

Laying-hen trials mean little if they last much less than 12 months and it was decided to look for similar effects in broilers. Earlier work on broilers had shown such effects but these had largely been ignored as individual experiments had shown no significant responses. Nevertheless, there was reason to believe that lower inclusion rates might give more promising results and an intensive investigation of broiler responses to dietary 'Pruteen' incorporation was set in motion.

This conjecture proved to be right and since that time more than thirty fully replicated trials have shown that 2 to 3% inclusions of 'Pruteen' in broiler diets give improvements in growth rate and in feed conversion efficiency of 1 to 2%. These improvements may appear to be small, but in the highly competitive and efficient broiler business they are of the greatest significance [8].

Later it was found that turkeys also gave better commercial performance with small inclusions of 'Pruteen' in the diet.

In 1969/70, when the Jealott's Hill work started, a large programme of animal feeding trials was anticipated but no-one foresaw the oil crisis and the effects this would have on the economics of the process. In the event the results of the trial work and the improvements in growth rate and feed conversion efficiency played an important part in carrying the project through a period of doubt. These nutritional improvements made a vital contribution to the overall economic viability of the project and the decision of Agricultural Division to enter into an exciting new business.

References

[1] Gow J S, Littlehailes J D, Smith S R L, Walker R B (1975) 'SCP from methanol bacteria' in *Single Cell Protein II*. Eds. Tannenbaum S R & Wang D I C

[2] van der Wal P (1976) 'Experience with SCP in animal feeding in Europe' *PAG Bull.* **6** (3), 7

[3] Braude R, Rhodes D N (1977) ' 'Pruteen'. A new source of protein for growing pigs. II Feeding trial: growth rate, feed utilisation & carcase and meat quality'. *Livest. Prod. Sci.* **4**, 91–100

[4] Schulz E, Oslage H J (1976) 'Composition and nutritive value of single cell protein (SCP)' *Anim. Feed Sci. & Technol.* **1**, 9

[5] Vogt H, Harnisch S, Torges H G (1975) 'Bakterien protein (Methanol-fermentations-protein) im geflugelfutter' *Archiv. fur Geflugelkunde* **4**, 146

[6] Roth F X, Kirchgessner M (1976) 'Methanol-fermentation protein in veal calf nutrition' *Anim. Feed Sci. & Technol.* **1**, 33

[7] Stobo I J F, Roy J H B (1977) 'The use of microbial protein in milk substitute diets for calves' *Proc. BASP* 143

[8] Bougon M (1976) 'Interet du 'Pruteen' dans l'alimentation des pondeuses' *Bull. Inf. Stn Expl d'aviculture de Plougragan, France* **16** (3) 91–96

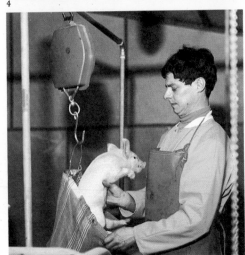

4

5

Single-cell protein

1 The pilot plant
2 and 3 Feeding trials with calves
   and pigs
4 Laboratory fermenters
5 Weighing piglet

Aerial view of Jealott's Hill 1977

Chapter 16

Perspective

In their accounts of research at Jealott's Hill, the writers have been at pains to record the part played by individuals who, through the years, have made the Station what it is, and who were responsible for the advances in agricultural science that have been described.

Some of these individuals were rewarded by recognition, in scientific circles, of their contribution. Four were elected to Fellowship of the Royal Society (M S Bartlett, G E Blackman, W R Boon, P W Brian). Nine were appointed to University Chairs (M S Bartlett, G E Blackman, P W Brian, J R Busvine, S H Crowdy, M J Geoghegan, Martin Jones, L A Summers, S J Watson) and visiting Professorships were conferred on W R Boon and J T Braunholtz. Three became Directors of other Institutes (G E Blackman, H J Page, D Rudd Jones).

Others received civil honours (S W Cheveley OBE; W Gavin Kt, CBE; R A Hamilton CBE; G Watts Padwick OBE; H J Page OBE, CMG; W G Templeman OBE; and S J Watson Kt, CBE).

Official recognition came also to the Company with the introduction in 1966 of the Queen's Award to Industry. Awards were gained by ICI Plant Protection for export achievement in the years 1967, 1970 and 1976, for technological innovation in the years 1973 (the fungicide 'Milstem'), 1974 (direct drilling with 'Gramoxone') and 1977 (the aphicide 'Pirimor') and one (1968) was shared between Mond and Organics Divisions for the development of bipyridyl production technology.

All who worked at Jealott's Hill during this time, however, were rewarded by the knowledge that what they were doing was worthwhile, that they enjoyed doing it, and that, to a greater or lesser extent, it was successful. All were motivated by the excitement of working at and across advancing frontiers of science.

The successful outcome of long-term research demands high standards and depends on a blend of team work and individual contribution. Agricultural research depends also on a mixture of basic sciences and technology.

The basic sciences form the framework for discovery which technology clothes with practicability; but this framework is often inadequate and insecure, and the links connecting it to discovery may be hard to perceive—frequently they are constructed after, rather than before, the event. Research programmes must, therefore, seek to use scientific knowledge where it is available and to generate it where it is not; and to be flexible enough to allow room for serendipity. Herein lies the perennial problem of research management. Rarely is any one laboratory capable of, or able to afford to undertake, more than a small fraction of the basic research that will in the long term prove vital to its planned, rather than accidental, growth. Can such a deficiency be made good, or should its effects be masked (at least in the short term) by ever-increasing investment in chance or random screening? Jealott's Hill has to some extent backed both horses, but with the conscious intention of establishing and supporting a group of scientific 'gatekeepers', pursuing long-term research topics of direct relevance to the Station's practical objectives and at the same time providing links with workers in the universities and other research institutes.

Biochemistry, for example, with the recent appointment of R S Morrod as section manager, and drawing on the expertise of B C Baldwin, J S Holden, D K Lawrence and S M Ridley, is increasingly concerned with basic science. Its contributions fall into three main groups: mode of action studies—experimental investigation of the primary act of a new molecule, preferably at biochemical rather than physiological level, and including attempted identification of the active component of the molecule in order to make direct contribution to the design of future synthetic programmes: investigation and operation of a limited number of biochemical screens, showing up effects such as inhibition of photosynthesis, prevention of protein synthesis, or interference with chitin metabolism, in order to supplement whole-organism screening especially in difficult areas such as plant growth regulator research: and a certain amount of fundamental work—for example, on the biochemistry of target weeds—that may lead to new intuitions about possible means of control.

Such work, in other research fields as well as in biochemistry, is responsible for the Station's links with science in the outside world. These are now widespread, and PPD participates actively with universities and other research establishments in the UK in over thirty joint projects. Some are CASE awards, some are wholly sponsored by the Division, and four are carried out under awards made by the ICI Corporate Joint Research Scheme; subjects range from plant breeding to specific organic synthesis. There are, as yet, few comparable joint projects with establishments overseas though there are some; examples would include one on organic synthesis with the Commonwealth Scientific and Industrial Research Organisation in Australia and one on soil science and direct drilling with the Instituto Agronomico do Paraná, in Brazil. There is also a great deal of collaborative activity in the applied sciences, as a result of which greatly valued working associations have been developed between Jealott's Hill and a substantial number of agricultural research establishments in the UK and overseas.

Beyond the laboratory and field plot, these links with the outside world are extended and strengthened in a variety of ways. Outstanding amongst these has been the recognition, in January 1969, of Jealott's Hill Research Station as an Associated Institution of the University of Reading. (The title of Visiting Professor may in addition be conferred on the Director for as long. as the association continues). This has brought benefits both tangible and intangible; opportunities for staff to contribute to the specialist teaching of particularly relevant university courses, sharing of research or library facilities, participation in university seminars and special symposia, and pooling of contacts and experience especially in relation to overseas development activities.

Members of staff have, in the nature of things played a specialist advisory or part-time teaching role in many other universities from time to time in the past. Recent examples include Brunel, East Anglia, Bristol, Surrey and London. Other, more personal, links have been established with Nottingham University through membership of the School of Agriculture Advisory Board, and with UK agricultural research institutions such as Rothamsted, Long Ashton, the Weed Research Organisation and the Glasshouse Crops Research Institute through membership of the Visiting or Advisory Groups.

All of this adds up—without attempting to present an exhaustive catalogue—to a picture of solid involvement with, and working access to, UK centres of teaching and research in agriculture and related sciences. Such is only to be expected of an establishment with the history, resources and aspirations of Jealott's Hill; and the Station's dependence on, and wish to promote outside activity in, selected areas of biological and biochemical science is likely to increase in the future rather than diminish. Associated with this will be the continued help of ICI's distinguished consultants, to extend the range of effective experience and judgement beyond the scope of existing full-time staff.

So much for the past. The integrity called for by Keeble has been guarded jealously, though not exclusively—both the long-term prosperity of agriculture and the immediate interests of the Company have been served. What of the future?

Integrity without purpose will not serve; but if purpose is universally equated to short-term or unduly narrow objectives, the full value and potential of the Station will equally not be realised. Which is only another way of saying that in the broadest sense the philosophical problems of research management at Jealott's Hill remain much as they have always been: awareness of needs (opportunities), realistic appraisal of technical feasibilities, and a judicious and light handed stimulation of high standards of scientific quality and personal commitment.

In detail, however, things must be expected to change. Whilst there is good reason to suppose that the absolute frequency of appearance of new products from the crop protection industry is decreasing, it does not at all follow that this trend applies to the rate of major innovation; indeed, over the last two or three years the reverse appears to be the case and it is reasonable to suppose that we are in fact entering a period of discovery of much more active ($\times 10$—$\times 50$) molecules, which will be significantly more costly to manufacture and in which efficiency, selectivity and environmental benefits will be accompanied by greater demands upon formulation and economic delivery to the target. Research and development costs will continue to rise, and in the face of all these factors commercial success over the 10–20 year span will go more and more to the sophisticated chemistry-based organisation with the will and ability to call upon scientific resources to direct a progressive move away from 'blunderbuss research'. It should be borne in mind that today's discovery will not be commercially significant in less than ten years!

But during the next ten years the research process itself at Jealott's Hill is likely to change more than it has since the late 1960s, in preparation for the technologies of the twenty-first century. Crop protection will still, as a rule, be achieved by our exogenous synthetic molecules, but these will increasingly act as 'trigger' or control agents, rather than in situ toxophores, possibly at second hand as in the controlled modification of genetic transmission. Economy and precision of placement of chemicals will become increasingly important, with consequent implications for the skills of those charged with the development of new application equipment. The rôle of industry in the evolution of biological control methods is still unsure; Jealott's Hill will continue to keep abreast of developments, sometimes by direct participation in selected research areas, but it would be foolhardy to predict any deep commitment in the course of the next ten years.

It is appropriate that the fiftieth anniversary of Jealott's Hill has been marked by the completion and occupation of a new Environmental Sciences building; apart from recalling an organisation and operational 'first' for ICI ten years ago, and giving due weight to the importance of ecological, metabolic and residue studies in the process of product development, it will perhaps help to re-direct attention towards a total systems (or 'agricultural') view of crop protection. Management rather than extermination of pests is likely to be a subject of increasing interest to the farmer and grower of the future, and in this field, as in others, Jealott's Hill will maintain its ability to contribute authoritatively to the main streams of developing agriculture technology.

Subject Index

Abbott Laboratories, 57, 59
Abol Ltd, 2
'Abol X' (see menazon),
acetylcholine, 50
acetylcholinesterase inhibition, 49, 50
Achillea millefolium (yarrow), 36
'Actellic' (see pirimiphos-methyl)
Aedes aegypti (mosquito), 52
Aelia sp (cereal bug), 101
Africa, cotton blackarm, desert locust, 110
Agricultural Development & Advisory
   Service of the UK. (ADAS), 93, 95, see
   also NAAS
Agricultural Division (ICI) 8, 9, 65, 137,
   138, 144
Agricultural Research Council of the UK,
   5, 36
Agriotes spp (wireworms), 6, 34, 44, 45, 106
'Agrocide' (see BHC)
Agropyron repens (couch grass), 79, 81
'Agrosan' seed dressings, 29, 110
Agrostis spp. (bent grass) in permanent
   pastures, 78
'Agrosol' seed dressing, 31
'Agroxone' (MCPA), 38
Akers Research Laboratories (ICI) 7, 55,
   56, 62, 87
Albright & Wilson Ltd, 49
aldrin, 45, 106
Alkali & Chemical Corporation of India
   (ACCI), 116
Alkali (now Mond) Division of ICI, 130
American Chemical Paint Company
   (Amchem), 38
American Cyanamid Company, 51
2-aminopyrimidine systemic fungicides,
   discovery 88–90, dimethirimol 88, 90–
   92, ethirimol 88, 92–95, bupirimate 88,
   95–97
amiton, 8, 50–51, 119–20, 125
amitrole, prior to paraquat treatment, 82
anhydrous ammonia, 17
anniversary, twentyfifth, 61
annual nettle *(Urtica urens)*, 68
Anthonomus pomorum (apple blossom
   weevil), 45
Anthonomus grandis (cotton boll weevil), 102
Anti-Locust Research
   Organisation/Centre, 44, 47
antibiotics, as systemic fungicides, 87
Aonidiella aurantii (citrus scale), 110
aphids 2, 107, on apple 53, beans 53, 108,
   brassicas 53, cereals, chrysanthemum
   108, hops 43, lettuce 107, 109, pea 52,
   107, peach 108, potato 53, soft fruit 53,
   sugar beet 52–53, 108, top fruit 45,
   vegetables 108
'Aphox' (pirimicarb), 109
apple, aphids 53, blossom weevil 45,
   codling moth 101, powdery mildew 87,
   95, 96, sawfly 45
aquatic weed control, diquat and
   paraquat, 75
Argentina, cattle ticks, sheep mange mite
   106, pasture, fodder crops, direct
   drilling 113, wheat, minimum
   cultivation 113
arsenic, 2, 5
artichokes (globe), earlier with GA, 58
Atomaria linearis (pygmy mangold beetle),
   102
atrazine, mixtures with paraquat, 81
Australia, crop desiccation 113–4, field
   screening station 114–7, fire-break
   defoliation, diquat 72, gibberellic acid
   on seedless grapes 58, pasture and
   fodder crops direct drilling 80, 113,
   wheat, minimum cultivation 113
auxins (phytohormones), 35

bacillus subtilis, 130
banana, delayed ripening with GA 59,
   weed control, paraquat/diuron 82,
   weevil 106
barley (see also cereals), accelerated
   malting with GA 56, direct drilling 79,
   effects of rotation 13, nitrogen response
   of new varieties 15, powdery mildew 92–95
Batrachedra amydraula (date palm moth),102
Bayer Leverkusen, 107, see also Farben IG
beans, aphids 53, 108, *Fusarium* 31, *Pythium*
   31, seed fly 105, seed treatment 31, 37
Bemisia tabaci (whitefly) on cotton, Turkey
   101
benzene hexachloride (BHC, 666), 6, 34,
   42–48, discovery of insecticidal action
   43–44, 47, laboratory tests and field
   experiments 43–44, identification of
   gamma isomer 44, 119, BHC and
   BHC/organomercurial seed treatments
   34–55, taint in certain crops 46, control
   of cocoa capsid, desert locust 111, spray
   programme, top fruit 45, malaria
   eradication 46, smoke generators 46, fly
   resistance 46-7
benzimidazole systemic fungicides, 88
Billingham Division (ICI) 2, 4, 8, 9, 17,
   18, 23, 26 see also Agric. Div. at end of
   entry
binapacryl, 96
biochemistry inputs, 146
Biological Research Centre (ICI America)
   118
2,2'-bipyridylium dibromide (see diquat)
bipyridylium herbicides, 8, 67–97 (see also
   diquat, paraquat, morfamquat)
birds, breeding territories, mapping, 122,
   narcotics (tribromo- &
   trichloroethanol), 119, 134, repellents,
   ('Corvusine', 'gas black', gas tar/pitch),
   133–4
black pod, cocoa *(Phytophthora palmivora)*,
   111

black currant, BHC taint, 46, powdery mildew, 87
blackarm, cotton *(Xanthomonas malvacearum)*, 110–11
Blackley see Dyestuffs Div. (ICI)
Blechnum (fern), 77
Blissus spp (chinch bugs), 106
blister blight, tea *(Exobasidium vexans)*, 110
bone meal (see organic manures)
The Boots Co. Ltd, 39
Bothynoderes punctiventris (sugar beet weevil), 102
Boyce Thompson Institute (USA), 35
Brassica sinapis (yellow charlock), 36
brassicas, aphids 53, flea beetle 34, 44, cabbage root fly 105
Brazil, field screening station, 115–8, wheat/soya, direct drilling 113
Bristol University, 147
British Dyestuffs Corporation, 29
British Oil Cake Manufacturers Ltd, 140
British Petroleum Ltd, 137
British Sulphate of Ammonia Federation, 2
British Trust for Ornithology, 122
Brixham Laboratory (Marine Biology Laboratories of ICI), 75, 120, 121
bromacil, synergist for paraquat, 82
Broom's Barn Experimental Station (UK), 52
Brunel University, 147
Brunner, Mond & Co, 2, 12
Brussels sprouts, effect of organic manures v. sulphate of ammonia, 17
buffalo grass *(Paspalum conjugatum)*, 76, 81, 82
bupirimate, discovery 88–90, development 96, properties 96, metabolites of, 123, mildew control on apple 96, cucurbits, peaches, roses 97
Byturus tomentosus (raspberry beetle), 43

cabbage see brassicas
Cambridge University, School of Agriculture, 22
Canada, effect of GA on cherries, rhubarb 58, minimum cultivation cereals and fodder crops, 113
capsicums, aphids, 109
capsids, on top fruit 45, cocoa 111
captafol, 87
captan, 87, 95
carrots, BHC taint 46, carrot fly 105, soil-less culture 132
castor bean, desiccation 75
cattle, grassland management 18–21, strip and paddock grazing 19, 21, set-stocking (continuous grazing) 123, two-field and full-graze systems 21, at the Leaths 25, single-suckler beef at Wilton 26, zero-grazing at Dairy House 26, farmlet system at Henley Manor 25, 26, high nitrogen and animal health 19, metabolic studies, bipyridyls in cows 123–4, single-cell protein, calves 143–4
Central Agricultural Control of ICI

(CAC) 6, 8, 10, 26, 63, 110
Central Toxicology Laboratories of ICI (CTL) 83, 91, 140, 141, see also IHRL
Centrosema, 77
cereals, aphids 109, bunt, smut and leaf stripe 29–30, 31, direct drilling 79–80, effect of nitrogen 79, effect on seed rate 79, winter cereals 80, effects of rotation on yields and soil fertility 13, weeds in 36, trials with MCPA and 2,4-D 37, trials with low volume sprayer 38, wheat and barley yield increases in 50 years 27
'Ceresol' seed dressing 31
Ceylon (now Sri Lanka) blister blight of tea 110
chemical ploughing (see paraquat, direct drilling)
Cheshunt Experimental Station (UK) 2
Chenopodium album (fat hen), 36
Chevron Chemical Company, 80, 113
chickweed *(Stellaria media)*, 39
chinch bug *(Blissus* spp), 106
Chipman Chemical Company Inc, 72, 75
chrysanthemum, aphids 108, soil-less culture 132
Chrysanthemum segetum (corn marigold), 36
citrus, GA, delayed ripening of orange and lemon fruits 57, GA, fruit set in mandarins and clementines 57, 58, GA, preservation of green-ness in limes 58, minimum cultivation 113, scale insects 110
cleavers *(Galium aparine)*, 39
Cochliotis melolonthoides (sugar cane weevil) 106
cockroaches 103
cocoa, capsids 47, 111, black pod 111
codling moth, pirimiphos-methyl trials France 101
coffee, weed control, paraquat/diuron 82
Colonial Office/Service (UK Government) 44, 47, 63, 110, 111, 113
Columba columbus (wood pigeon) 134
Commonwealth Scientific and Industrial Research Organisation, of Australia (CSIRO) 146
Computer Systems, ASSASSIN, BCDF, CROSSBOW, KWIC, 65
Concentrated complete fertilizer (CCF) 15
conifers, earlier flowering with GA 59
Cooper, William 2, Cooper & Nephews 2
Cooper, McDougall & Robertson Ltd, 2, 5, 8, 47
Co-operative Awards for Science & Engineering (CASE), UK 145
copper fungicides, control of animal health problems 4, potato blight 4, cotton blackarm 110, cocoa blackpod 111, cuprous oxide ('Perecot') 33
copper sulphate 2, 35
corn buttercup *(Ranunculus arvensis)*, 36
corn marigold *(Chrysanthemum segetum)*, 36
corn spurrey *(Spergula arvensis)*, 36
Corporate Laboratory (ICI) 138
Cosmopolites sordidus (banana weevil), 106

Costelytra zealandica (New Zealand grass grub) 106
cotton, black arm 110–111, boll weevil 102, desiccation 75, whitefly 101
couch grass *(Agropyron repens),* 79, 81
cucumber, bean seed fly 105, powdery mildew 89, 90
cucurbits (cucumbers and melons) mildew 97
cuprous oxide ('Perecot'), 33, cotton blackarm 110–11
cyanide fumigation 5, 110
Czechoslovakia, rape desiccation 74, direct drilling 113

DD mixture (dichloropropenes/dichloropropanes) 135
DDT 6, 45, 46, 103, 105
date palm, moth 102
defoliation, fire-breaks, USA, Australia 72
demeton-methyl 107
Denkavit B.V. 140
Derris, aphids 2, caterpillars 2, pests of top fruit 45
desiccants, oilseed crops, diquat 74–54, potatoes, dinoseb 73, diquat 73–74, sodium arsenite, sodium chlorate, sulphuric acid 73
Development Farms (ICI) 10, 11, 14, 21, 25, 26, 56
2,4-dichlorophenoxyacetic acid (2,4-D) 6, 36–39
dieldrin, soil pests replacement for 105, 45
di-isopropyl fluorophosphonate 49
dimefox 49
dimethirimol, discovery 8, 88–90, properties (translocation) 90, metabolites of, residue analysis 125, formulation for melon fields 91, mildew control on barley 92, cucurbits 91, resistance of mildew strains to 91, 94
1,1'-dimethyl-4,4'-bipyridylium dichloride (see paraquat)
Dinitro-orthocresol (DNC) DNOC, insecticide dormant spray 45, oilseed crop desiccant 74
dinocap 95, 96
dinoseb, potato haulm desiccant 73, oilseed crop desiccant 74
'Diothyl' (pyrimithate), 88, 98
diquat, discovery 8, 67, interaction with soil especially soil colloids 69, mode of action, properties 68–70, defoliation of fire breaks 72, desiccation of clovers, closed-boll cotton, lucerne 72, potatoes (haulm desiccation, palatability to cattle, residue levels in tubers, stem-end rot) 72–74, development overseas 112, metabolism in cows, goats, sheep 123–4, residue analysis, ion-exchange chromatography 125, selectivity in cereals 71–2, related to redox potential 83, weed control-aquatic, industrial, limitations for, summer fallow, in

rubber 72, 75, 76–7
disease resistance, mildew resistance to dimethirimol 91, 94, ethirimol 94–95
Distantiella theobroma (capsid) 111
dithiocarbamate fungicides 87
diuron, paraquat/diuron, industrial weed control 75, advantages 81, paraquat/diuron, perennial weed control in bananas, coffee, orchards, sugar cane, rubber and oil plantations 82
dodecyltrimethyl ammonium bromide 67
drazoxolon, fungicide, seed treatment 31–32, 87, spray treatment 31–32, 87, 95
E I du Pont de Nemours & Co. (Inc.), 31, 88, 136
Dyestuffs Division (ICI) 5, 7, 8, 29, 31, 36, 37, 49, 51, 55, 61, 65, 91, 134

earthworms 122
earwigs 103
East Africa Agricultural & Forestry Research Organisation (EAAFRO) 110
East Anglia, University of 147
East Malling Research Station (UK) 2
ecology (see environmental studies)
Edinburgh University 6, 140
Edward Grey Institute of Ornithology (UK) 134
Egypt, gibberellic acid on seedless grapes 58
elemental sulphur 95
Eli Lilly & Co, 57
Empire Cotton Growing Corporation 101
Encarsia formosa (Chalcid) 109
Endeavour 64
Environmental Protection Agency of the USA (EPA) 120
environmental studies 119–127, ecology 120–122, birds and small mammals 122, earthworms 122, ecotank system (Metcalf) 122, effect of herbicides on aquatic systems 121, microarthropods, soil sampling 121, soil fauna 121, surface-dwelling invertebrates 122
pesticide metabolism 122–124, application of gas/liquid chromatography 124, 125, nitrogen selective detectors 125, cholinesterase inhibition 125, fate of pesticides in animals and foodstuffs 123–4, ion-exchange chromatography 125, radio-labelling 122–4, residue analysis, technique development 124, use of mass spectrometry 124
requirements of registration authorities 127
residue analysis, ion-exchange and gas/liquid chromatography 124, 125, nitrogen selective, flame photometric, and electron-capture detectors 126, mass fragmentography 126, technique development 124
soil studies 126–7, behaviour of bipyridyls in soil 126, degradation of paraquat by *Lipomyces* sp. 126, effect of pesticides on respiration and nitrification 126, fate of fertilizers 126

toxicology 120
Eriosoma lanigerum (woolly aphid) 45
Erysiphe graminis (powdery mildew) 89, 92–95
ethirimol, discovery 8, 88–90, formulation as coated fertilizer granule 92, seed dressing 92 (col 93–4), combined with captafol 94, mildew control on barley and wheat 92–5, field trials 92–3, resistant mildew strains 94–5, metabolism 123, residues 125
ethyl mercury chloride (EMC) 30, 45
Eupatorium odoratum 77
European Economic Community (EEC) 142
Eurygaster (cereal bug) on wheat 101
Exobasidium vexans (tea blister blight) 110
experimental chemicals, formulation 117, packaging and labelling 117, shipment 117
Explosives Division, see Nobel Division (ICI)

Farben IG (IG Farbenfabriken Bayer) 29, 49
farm management (ICI systems) 'Cashplan' 27, costed farm scheme 26, 'Dairymaid' 27, grassland management investigation 26, 'MASCOT' system 26–27, Monthly Recorded Farm Scheme 27, recorded farm investigation 26
fat hen *(Chenopodium album),* 36
fensulphothion 106
fenuron, synergist for paraquat 82
'Fernasan' (seed dressings) 31
Fernhurst 7, 8, 32, 40, 45, 51, 63, 64, 72, 75, 80, 84, 93, 104, 110, 127
ferns, in oil palm, Malaysia 77
fertilizers, concentrated complete, CCF 5, 15; nitrogenous, ammonium nitrate 12, ammonium sulphate 15–16, liquid 17, 'Nitram' 16, 'Nitro-chalk 15–16, urea 16; slow release (nitrogen), ammeline, ammelide 18, 'Gold-N' (sulphur-coated urea) 18, guanidine salts 18, isobutylidene diurea (IBDU) 18, shoddy, meat and bone-meal, hoof-meal, fish-meal, guano, dried blood 17, oxamide 18
field poppy *(Papaver rhoeas),* 36
field screening stations, overseas 114–7
fir (Douglas) increased seed production with gibberellins 59
fish-meal (see organic manures)
flax soil-borne diseases 31
flea beetle *(Phyllotreta* spp) 6, 34, 43, 44
fleas pirimiphos-methyl aerosol, 103
Florida, University of 57
Food & Agriculture Organisation of the United Nations (FAO) 47, 104, 109
Food & Drug Administration of the USA (FDA) 125
forage conservation, 22–25

formulation technology 65, 66, 82, 93, 101, 103, 109, 117
France, field experiments with fungicides 90, insecticides 101, 104, 105, minimum cultivation/direct drilling 113, field screening station 114–7
fruit (soft) aphids 53
Fusarium spp. 31

Galium aparine (cleavers) 39
'Gammacol' (BHC) formulation 65
'Gammalin' (BHC) 111
'Gammexane' (BHC) 44
General Chemicals Division (ICI) 5, 6, 42, 47, 49, 61, 85, 122, 135
Germany, cockroaches 103, sugar beet aphid 108, wheat, maize, minimum cultivation 113
Ghana (formerly Gold Coast) cocoa black pod, capsid 111, cotton seed treatment 33
Gibberella fujikuroi, 55, 60
gibberellic acid (GA) 7, isolation 55, manufacturing licensees 57, uses on: artichokes (globe), barley, cherries, citrus, grapes, hops, limes, ornamentals, pasture, pears, potatoes, rhubarb, watercress 56–58
gibberellins A_4/A_7 on bananas, conifers 59
Glasshouse Crops Research Institute (UK) 106, 109, 133, 147
glasshouses, bupirimate on indoor roses 97, dimethirimol soil treatment 90, integrated control of pests in, 109, pirimicarb smoke 109, pirimiphos-methyl fogging 101
Globodera (Heterodera) rostochiensis (potato root eelworm) 135
goats, fate of bipyridyls in, 123–4
'Gold-N' (see nitrogen)
grain weevil *(Sitophilus granarius),* 44, 104
'Gramonol' (paraquat plus monolinuron), 82
'Gramoxone' (see paraquat)
grapes (seedless) increased size with GA, 57, 58
grass, seed treatment 87, soil-borne diseases 32
grass (dried) 5, 22, 23
grass weeds 40, limitations of diquat 75, in rubber, Malaysia 76–77, 81
grassland, effect of light 13, temperature 12, nitrogen 12, 16, 18, grazing (sward management) 12, rotations 13, pasture renovation/direct drilling 78–9, GA 56
grazing systems: cattle 19, 20, sheep 20, paddock and strip grazing 21, zero-grazing 21, farmlet system 25, 123 or 2-field system, full-graze system 21, management: early and late bite 5, grass/clover swards 14, 15, nitrogen in drainage water 19–20, nitrogen effect on animal health 19
greater plantain *(Plantain major),* 36
Greece, GA on seedless grapes 58

griseofulvin, 7, 87
groundnut, bean seed fly 105
guanidine salts, as slow release fertilizer 18

Hawthorndale Laboratories of ICI 2, 3,
    5, 6, 29, 31, 42, 43, 44, 64, 110
hay, crude-protein content 22
heptachlor 45
herbicides (selective) 35–41
Herpotogramma spp (webworms) 106
hexachlorbenzene (HCB) 31
hexachlorocyclohexane (HCH, BHC) 42
Holland, dimethirimol fungicide 91,
    rhubarb, dormancy break with GA 58,
    sugar beet aphid 108
hoof-meal (see organic manures)
hops, aphids 43, seedless, yield increased
    by GA 58
Hoplocampa testudinea (apple sawfly) 45
Hungary, agreement with State Office for
    Development 113, direct drilling,
    minimum cultivation 113, winter wheat,
    mildew 94
Hylemyia (Delia) antiqua (onion fly) 105
Hylemyia cilicrura (Delia platura) bean seed
    fly 105
Hylemyia (Erioischia) brassicae (cabbage root
    fly) 105

ICI America (ICI US) Agricultural
    Chemicals Division 117, 120
ICI Australia & New Zealand (ICIANZ)
    88, 89
ICI Malaya (ICI Malaysia) 75, 76
Imperata cylindrica (lalang) 76
India, diquat on potato 73, field screening
    station 114–7, rice, minimum
    cultivation 113, tea, blister blight 110
β-indoleacetic acid (IAA) 35–36
β-indolebutyric acid 35
Industrial Hygiene Research Laboratories
    (ICI) 50, 120, see also CTL
industrial weed control, diquat 72,
    paraquat and mixtures with residuals 75
Infestation Control Laboratory (UK
    Ministry of Agriculture) 135
insect resistance to BHC 46, DDT 46, 103,
    dieldrin 105, malathion 104, multiple
    OP resistance 109
Institut für Kleintierzucht Braunschweig.
    (W. Germany) 141
Instituto Agronomico do Parana,
    (IAPAR) Brazil 146
Instituut voor Biologisch en Scheikundig
    Onderzoek van Landbouwgewassen,
    Wageningen (Holland) 84
Instituut voor Landbouwkundig
    Onderzoek van Biochemische
    Production, Wageningen, (Holland)
    140
integrated control; menazon, lack of effect
    on beneficial insects 53, pirimiphos-
    methyl no lasting effect on beneficial
    insects 103, pirimicarb selective effect

108, pirimicarb in glasshouse pest
    management 109, future attitudes in
    crop protection 148
intelligence services at Jealott's Hill 64–65
Iran, gibberellic acid on seedless grapes 58
Iraq, date palm moth, pirimiphos-methyl
    102, street fogging, Baghdad 103
isobutylidene diurea (IBDU), as slow
    release fertilizer 18
iso-propyl phenyl carbamate (IPC) 36,
    39–40, chlor- (CIPC) 40
Israel, artichokes (globe), advanced
    cropping with GA 58, clementines, fruit
    set with GA 58, dimethirimol fungicide
    use 91
Italy, artichokes (globe), advanced
    cropping with GA 58, peach aphid 108,
    vines, maize, rice, minimum cultivation
    113

Japan, gibberellins and gibberellic acid 55,
    dimethirimol fungicide, melons 91,
    pirimiphos-ethyl seed dressing 105
Japanese beetle *(Popillia japonica),* 106
Jordan, refuse dump spraying, Amman 103

kale, direct drilling 79–80
Kenya, cotton blackarm 111

lalang *(Imperata cylindrica)* 76
lead arsenate 45
Leptohylemia coarctata (wheat bulb fly) 106
lettuce, aphids 107
Leuconostoc dextranicum, 130
libraries at Jealott's Hill and Fernhurst 64,
    65
lime-sulphur 95
linseed, desiccation 75
Local Defence Volunteers (Home Guard) 6
(Locusta migratoria) locusts 6, 44, 51, 110
London University 121, 147
Long Ashton Research Station (UK) 2,
    146
Lygodium (fern) 77

Macrosiphum (Acyrthosiphon) pisum (pea
    aphid) 52, 107
McDougall Bros., McDougall &
    Robertson, McDougall & Yalding 2
machinery, direct drilling and paraquat
    special applications (see paraquat), low
    volume sprayers 38, seed dressing 32–
    34, 93, 111
maize, minimum cultivation, overseas 113
malaria eradication, BHC, DDT 46,
    pirimiphos-methyl 103
malathion 51, 103, 104
Malaysia, field screening station 114–7,
    mosquitoes 103, oil palm, weed control
    76–77, rice, minimum cultivation 113,
    rubber, weed control 76–77, 81, 82
maleic hydrazide 135
maneb 87
mange mite (sheep) 106

Marine Biology Laboratories, see Brixham Laboratories (ICI)

Melastoma malabathricum, (Straits rhododendron) 77

Meloidogyne spp (root knot nematodes) 136

melon, mildew control with dimethirimol, Spain 91

menazon, discovery 8, 51, 107, metabolic studies 123, mode of action 53, systemic activity, translocation 52, seed dressing 52–3, zero effect on beneficial insects 53

Merck & Co. (Inc) 57

'Mergamma' seed-dressings (BHC/mercury) 34, 45

Merrindale Laboratories (ICIANZ) 89

'Methoxone' (MCPA) 36

α-methoxyphenylacetic acid (MOPA) 135

2-methyl-4-chlorophenoxyacetic acid (MCPA) 6, 36–39, 40

methyl mercury dicyandiamide (MMD), 30–31

methyl mercury nitrile (MMN) 30

Methylophilus methylotrophus (methanol organism) 138

Mexico, crop desiccation 114

microarthropods 121

'Milcap' (ethirimol/captafol) 94

'Mil-Col' (drazoxolon), control of apple mildew 95, seed-dressing for peas and beans 32

'Milcurb' (see dimethirimol)

'Milgo' 'Milstem' (see ethirimol)

Ministry of Agriculture (UK) 5, 6, 93, 135

Mitsubishi Corporation 18

Mond Division (ICI) 145

Monks Wood Experiment Station (UK Institute of Terrestrial Ecology) 75, 121

Montecatini SA 52

Monsanto Chemical Company 130

monuron, combined with paraquat 81

Morocco, clementines, fruit set with GA 58

morfamquat, selectivity related to redox potential 83, weed control in cereals, turf 84

mosquito *(Aedes aegypti)* 52, 100, 103

Munich University 140

mushroom beds, Sciarid flies 105–6

Myzus persicae (peach /potato aphid) 108

α-naphthylacetic acid (NAA) 6, 35–36

β-naphthoxyacetic acid 36

National Agricultural Advisory Service of the UK (NAAS) see also ADAS 80, 83

National Institute for Research in Dairying, UK (NIRD) 131, 140

National Scientific Feed Association, Japan 141

Nature Conservancy, UK see Monks Wood Experiment Station

Nephrolepis (fern) 77

New Zealand, pasture and fodder crops, direct drilling 80, 113

New Zealand grass grub *(Costelytra zealandica)* 106

Nigeria, cocoa blackpod, capsid 111, cotton blackarm 33, 111, Dept. of Agriculture 111

'Nimrod' (see bupirimate) 96

'Nitram' (see nitrogen)

Nitram Ltd. 2, 3, 6, 12

'Nitro-Chalk', fertilizer (see nitrogen)

nitrogen, effect on animal health, in drainage water 19, forms of: straights and mixtures, liquid, slow release 15–18, on grassland 12, grass/clover 14–15

'No-till' (see paraquat, direct drilling)

Nobel Division (ICI) 46

'Nomersan' and 'Nomersan W' (seed dressings) 31

Nottingham University 140, 147

oak trees, *Tortrix viridiana* 102

oats (see also cereals), effects of rotation on yields and soil fertility 13, leaf stripe 29, rust 89, smut 29, wireworm 45, yellow charlock 36

oil palm, weed control 77, 82, 112

oilseed crops, desiccation 74–75

olive, moth 102

onion, fly 105

Oospora pustulans (skin spot) potatoes 40

Ophiobolus graminis (take-all) in winter wheat 13

organic manures, shoddy, meat and bone meal, etc. v. sulphate of ammonia on Brussels sprouts 17

Organics Division 145, see also Dyestuffs Division (ICI)

Organisation of Petroleum Exporting Countries (OPEC) 142

organochlorine insecticides, see BHC, DDT, aldrin, dieldrin, insect resistance

organo-mercurial – see seed dressings

organophosphorus insecticides see TEPP, amiton, dimefox, dimethoate, malathion, menazon, parathion, pyrimidine phosphates, schradan

ornamentals, better quality with GA 58

Outlook on Agriculture 64

oxamyl 136

oxathiin systemic fungicides 88

'PP Kumakate' (BHC) 111

Palestine, citrus scale 110

Panicum nodosum (buffalo grass) 76

Panonychus ulmi (red spider mite) 50

Papaver rhoeas (field poppy) 36

'Paracol' (paraquat plus diuron) 82

paraoxon 50

paraquat, discovery 67, evaluation and development 111–4, formulation – cols 82, granules to prevent misuse 83, metabolism (degradation with Lipomyces) 126, fate in animals 123–4, mode of action (interaction with soil) 126, Hill reaction of photosynthesis 81, uptake and translocation 70, 71, properties 68–70, precautions against mis-use 83, residue analysis 125, ion exchange chromatography 125

paraquat applications, aquatic weed control 75, control of weeds in crops 76–77, 82, 112, crop desiccation 113–4, direct drilling 77–80, industrial weed control 75–76, minimum cultivation 113, pasture renovation 78–9, selective use 78

paraquat machinery developments, application equipment: 'Arbogard', dribble-bar, 'Fido', 'Intarow', 'Polyrow', 'Unirow', 'Vari-row', 'Vibrajet', 'Vibro-boom', 'Xpando' 85 direct drills: Bettinson 80, 85, Gibbs Kale drill, Howard Stanhay direct drill 85, JEC 'Grasslands' sod-seeder 79, 84, modified Massey-Ferguson combine drill 79, Moore Uni-drill, WMF Howard Rotaseeder 85

paraquat mixtures, with monuron 81, diuron, simazine 75, 81–82, atrazine, fenuron, bromacil 81, terbacil, monolinuron, allachlor, metribuzin 82, preceded by amitrole 82, synergism 81–2

parathion 49, 50

Paspalum conjugatum (buffalo grass) 76, 81, 82

peach, mildew 97, aphid 108

pear, increased fruit set with GA after frost damage 57, 58

peas, aphids 52, bean seed fly 105, *Fusarium* 31, *Pythium* 31, seed treatment 31, 87, soil-less culture 132

perchloroethylene 'heavy ends' 135

'Perecot' 45, (cuprous oxide) 33, 110–11

Pest Control Research Committee (ICI) 5, 49

Pfizer (Inc) 57

Pharmaceuticals Division (ICI) 9, 20, 55, 57, 65, 88, 89, 98, 138

β-phenoxybutyric acid 39

α-phenoxypropionic acid 39

'Perenox' (copper fungicide) 110, 111

phenyl mercury acetate (PMA) 30, 45

Philippines, field screening station 114–7

photography 66

phthalimide fungicides 87

Phyllotreta spp (flea beetle) 6, 34, 43, 44

phytohormones (auxins) 35

Phytophthora infestans (potato blight) 2

Phytophthora palmivora (black pod, cocoa) 111

Phytoseiulus persimilis (predatory mite) 109

pigs, single cell protein 140–4

pirimicarb, discovery 8, 99, 106–7, features (fumigant, systemic) 107, 108, formulation 109, metabolism 107, 123, residues 108, 125, specificity (integrated control) 109

pirimiphos-ethyl, discovery 8, 89, 99, 105, evaluation 105, formulations 105, metabolism 123, non-fungitoxicity 106,

properties (persistence) 105, residue analysis 125–6, control of flies, bugs and beetle pests 105–6, veterinary use 106

pirimiphos-methyl, discovery 8, 89, 99, evaluation 99–105, formulation 101–3, metabolism 123, properties (safety, fumigant, persistence) 100, 102, residue analysis 125–6, control of pest complexes 99–103, use in public health, stored products 103–5

'Pirimor (see pirimicarb)

Plant Breeding Institute (UK) 95

Plant Protection Division (PPD) of ICI 109, 113, 146, 147

Plant Protection Ltd. 5, 8, 9, 40, 43, 45, 47, 49, 57, 63, 72, 100, 106, 111, 112, 113, 120, 127

Plantago major (greater plantain) 36

Plantio Direto (see paraquat, direct drilling)

Plasmopara viticola (vine downy mildew) 117

Podosphaera leucotricha (apple powdery mildew) 87, 95, 96

Poland, cabbage root fly 105, onion fly 105, sunflower desiccation 74

Polygonum spp. (knotgrass, bindweed, redshank) 40

Popillia japonica (Japanese beetle) 106

poppy, desiccation 75

potato, dormancy break with GA 58, haulm desiccation (desiccants, including diquat 72–4, palatability to cattle 73, residue levels in tubers 73, stem end rot 73–4), pests and diseases (blight 4, aphids 53, 107, 108, skin spot 40, root eelworm 135), sprout inhibitors 40, soil-less culture 132, taint from BHC 45, weed control 82

poultry, single cell protein 140–4

powdery mildew, apples 87, 95, 96, barley 92–95, blackcurrants 87, cucumber 89, 90, wheat 89, 92

Prays oleellus (olive moth) 102

predatory mite *(Phytoseiulus persimilis)* 109

'Primicid' (see pirimiphos-ethyl)

'Pruteen' (see single cell protein)

Psila rosae (carrot fly) 105

public health pests 103–104

Puccinia graminis f. sp. *avenae* (oat rust) 89

Pueraria 77

Pyrenophora avenae (oat leaf stripe) 29

pyrimidine carbamates 106–7, structure-activity studies 107

pyrimidine fungicides 88–97

pyrimidine insecticides 98–109

pyrimidine phosphates, structural requirements for insecticidal activity 99, pirimiphos-ethyl 99, 105–106, pirimiphos methyl 99–105

pyrimithate 88, 98

Pythium spp. 31

Queen's Award to Industry 95, 109, 145

radish, desiccation 75, soil-less culture 132
Ranunculus arvensis (corn buttercup) 36
rape, desiccation 74
'Rapid' aerosol (pirimicarb) 109
raspberry beetle *(Byturus tomentosus)* 43
Reading University 147
registration requirements 127
rhubarb, dormancy break with GA 58
rice, minimum cultivation 113
Robertson of Oban 2
Rockefeller Foundation (USA) 46
Roger alias Jolyf 1
Romania, direct drilling, minimum
    cultivation 113
rose, mildew 97
Rothamsted Experimental Station (UK)
    1, 13, 17, 36, 121, 130, 147
Royal Agricultural College, Cirencester 1
Royal Agricultural Society of England 85
Royal Botanic Gardens, Kew 36
rubber, weed control, diquat and paraquat
    76–77, 81, 111, paraquat mixtures with
    soil residual and foliar translocated
    herbicides 81, 82, sodium arsenite 76
Rubber Research Institute of Malaya 5
Runcorn see General Chemicals Division
    (ICI)

'SAIsan' (drazoxolon seed dressing) 32
safety, laboratory design 63
safflower desiccation 75
Sahlbergella singularis (capsid) 111
salicylanilide fungicide 87
'Saphizon' (menazon) 53
Sardinia, BHC resistant flies 46–7,
    malaria eradication 46
Saudi Arabia, town-scale aerial and
    ground spraying 103–4
'Sayfos' (menazon) 53
scale insects 101, 110
Schistocerca gregaria (desert locust) 110
schradan 49, 53
Sciarid flies 105–6
scorpions 103
Scottish Agricultural Industries Ltd. 11,
    32
seed dressing machinery 32–34,
    'Plantector' 32, 33, 'Portector' cotton
    seed treater 33, 111, 'Rotostat' 33–34
seed dressings, dual-purpose: 'Ceresol'
    (mercury/heptachlor) 31, 'Mergamma'
    range (BHC/mercury) 6, 34, 45
    fungicidal: mercurial – 'Agrosan' range
    29, 30, 111, 'Agrosol 31, liquid mercurials
    30; non-mercurial – 'Fernasan',
    'Nomersan' (thiram) 31, 'Nomersan' W
    (thiram + HCB) 31, 'Perecot' (cuprous
    oxide) 110–111, 'SAIsan', 'Mil-Col'
    (drazoxolon) 32
    insecticidal: 'Gammasan (BHC) 34,
    pirimiphos-ethyl 105, 'Saphizon',
    'Sayphos' (menazon) 53
Septoria (leaf blotch) 94
sesame, desiccation 75

sheep, fate of bipyridyls in 123–4,
    management systems 20–21
Sheffield University 138
Shell Chemical Co. 135
'Shirlan' (salicylanilide) 87
Shirley Institute (UK) 87
shoddy (see organic manures)
silage 5–6, 22–23
simazine, paraquat/simazine industrial
    weed control 75, 81, vines 82
single cell protein, development of process,
    pilot plant fermenter 137–9, feeding and
    breeding trials calves, pigs, poultry 141–
    3, 143–4, manufacture and economics
    142, uses: in laying hen and broiler
    diets, turkeys, as calf milk-replacers 143–4
Sitophilus granarius (grain weevil) 44, 104
skin spot *(Oospora pustulans)* 40
slugs, associated with direct drilling 79
Société pour la Protection de l'Agriculture
    S.A. (SOPRA) 90
sod seeding (see paraquat, direct drilling)
sodium arsenite, as potato haulm
    desiccant 73, weed control in oil palm 77
sodium chlorate, as potato haulm
    desiccant 73, as oilseed desiccant 74
soil, effect of pesticides on respiration and
    nitrification 126, effect on soil structure
    of: grass roots 130, methods of straw
    disposal 13, rotations 13, micro-
    organisms and their metabolites 130,
    polymeric substances 120, soil
    'conditioners' 130, fate of fertilizers in
    soil 126, interaction of bipyridyls with
    soil colloids 126
soil-less culture 132–133
South Africa, gibberellic acid on seedless
    grapes 58, citrus, maize, vines,
    minimum cultivation 113
South America, paraquat/diuron, weed
    control in coffee, sugar cane, bananas
    82, see also Argentina, Brazil
soya beans, desiccation 75,
    paraquat/linuron, alachlor or
    metribuzin prior to direct drilling 82
Spain, clementines, fruit set with GA 58,
    dimethirimol trials 90, sugar beet aphid
    108, field screening station 114–7
Spergula arvensis (corn spurrey) 36
Sphaerotheca fuliginea (cucumber powdery
    mildew) 89, 90
spider mites, *Panonychus ulmi* 50,
    Tetranychus cinnabarinus 109
spiders 103
'Spray-Seed' (direct drilling) 84
Sri Lanka (Ceylon) tea, blister blight 110
Stellaria media (chickweed) 39
stored product pests 104–105, malathion
    resistance 104, pirimiphos-methyl
    104–105
Strathclyde, University of 138
straw, caustic soda treatment 5, 23, effect
    of methods of straw disposal on soil
    structure 13

streptomycin 87
suckers, *(Psylla)* on top fruit 45
sugar beet, aphids 52–53, beetles 102, seed dressings 34, 52–53, virus yellows 52–53
sugar cane, weed control, paraquat/diuron 82, weevil 106
sulphuric acid, as selective herbicide 35, as potato haulm desiccant 73, oilseed crop desiccant 74
sunflower, desiccation, Poland 74
Surrey, University of 147
swedes, BHC taint 46, flea beetle 43
sweet peas, soil-less culture 132
'Sylade' (silage additive) 24
Synthetic Ammonia and Nitrates Ltd 2
Syria, street fogging, Damascus 103

take-all (see *Ophiobolus graminis*)
Takeda Chemical Industries Ltd 57
Tanzania (Tanganyika) cotton blackarm 33, 111, sugar cane Scarabaeid 106
tar oil 45
tea, blister blight 110
Tennessee Valley Authority 18
terbacil, paraquat/terbacil, citrus 82
'Terraklene' (paraquat plus simazine) 82
tetraethyl pyrophosphate (TEPP) 49
'Tetram' (amiton) 8, 50–51, 119–20, 125
tetramethyl thiuram disulphide (thiram) 31
Tetranychus (telarius) cinnabarinus (spider mite) 50
thiram (TMTD) 31, 87
ticks (cattle) 106
Tilletia caries (wheat bunt) 29
tolyl mercury acetate (TMA) 30
Tortrix viridiana on oaks 102
toxicology see Central Toxicology Laboratories (ICI)
'Totacol' (paraquat plus diuron) 82
Trialeurodes vaporariorum (glasshouse whitefly) 101
1,3,5,tricyanophenylpentane 136
triazine herbicides, as synergists for paraquat 81
trichlorobenzene 42
2,4,5-trichlorophenoxyacetic acid (2,4,5-T) 39
'Tuberite' (IPC) 40
turf, chafers, chinch bugs, webworms 106
Turkey, gibberellic acid on seedless grapes 58, whitefly on cotton, pirimiphos-methyl 101
turnip, flea beetle 43, soil-less culture 132

USA, diquat uses: defoliation of firebreaks, direct drilling/minimum cultivation 80, 113, industrial weed control, pre-harvest desiccation 72; field screening stations 114–7, gibberellic acid use on fruit 57–8, mosquitoes 103, pirimiphos-ethyl seed dressing 105, turf pests 106, winter wheat, mildew 94
USSR, mosquito larvae 103, sugar beet weevil 102

Uganda, cotton blackarm 110–11, Department of Agriculture 110
unicellular algae, *Chlorella vulgaris* 131–2, 137
Uniroyal (Inc.) 88
United Nations Relief and Rehabilitation Administration (UNRRA) 47
Urtica urens (annual nettle) 68
urea 16, 18, 25
urease, hydrolysis of urea, inhibition of urease 16
urea herbicides, as synergists for paraquat 81
Uruguay, cattle ticks 106, sheep mange mite 106
Ustilago avenae (oat smut) 29

Verdley Estate, see Fernhurst
vines, downy mildew, France 117, minimum cultivation 113
virus, cherry yellow 58, sugar beet yellows 52–53

War Agricultural Executive Committee (WAEC) 6, 37
Washington State University 58
wasps 103
watercress, winter treatment with GA 58
webworms *(Herpotogramma* spp) 106
Weed Research Organization (WRO) 147
'Weedkiller for New Lawns' (morfamquat) 84
'Weedol' (paraquat) 83
West African Cocoa Research Institute (WACRI) 111
wheat (see also cereals), diseases – bunt 29, mildew 92, 95, take-all 13, effect of rotations on yield 13, first direct-drilling experiment 79, minimum cultivation overseas 113, nitrogen response of new varieties 15, pests – wireworm 45, bulb fly 106, cereal bug 101, studies on root performance 80, yield increases over fifty years 27
whiteflies, *Bemisia tabaci* 101, *Trialeurodes vaporariorum* 101, 109
Widnes Laboratory – see General Chemicals Division (ICI)
wireworm (*Agriotes* spp) 6, 34, 44, 45, 106
Woburn Experimental Station (UK) 2
Womens Land Army (UK) 133
woolly aphid *(Eriosoma lanigerum)* 45
World Health Organisation (WHO) 20, 47, 103

Xanthomonas malvacearum (cotton blackarm) 110–11

Yalding Manufacturing Co. 2
Yalding Works 31, 43, 65, 120, 125, 127
yarrow *(Achillea millefolium)* 36
yellow charlock *(Brassica sinapis)* 36
Yugoslavia, direct drilling, minimum cultivation 113, mosquitoes 103

Zeltia Agraria SA 90

Name Index

Allan A P, 5
Allen H P, 72, 80, [86]
Anderson J R, 16, 126
Armitage E R, 14, 19
Ashley M G, 125
Atkins Frances, 64
Attwood Evelyn, 7
Austin W G L, 75

Bailie J H, [28]
Bakermans W A P, 84
Bakker Tj, 140
Baldwin B C, 126, 146
Balls I J, 111
Baranyovits F L C, 51, 99, 101, 107, 108, [109]
Barker A S, 26
Barker M R, [118]
Bartlett M S, 3, 145
Bebbington R M, 92
Beech C R, 83
Beling H, 56
Bell E G, 130, 131
Bellingham F, 24
Bender H, 43
Bent K J, 62, 90, [97]
Bessel J E, 26, [28]
Binns E S, [109]
Bishop N D, 106
Blackman G E, 3, 5, 12, 13, [27] 145
Blaney L T, 57
Blewett W V, 5
Bloomfield A, 84, 111
Boon W R, 7, 8, 9, 61, 68, [85] 112, 125, 145
Borrow A, 55
Bougon M, [144]
Bovingdon H H S, 44
Bradbury F R, 47, [48] 122
Braude R, [144]
Braunholtz J T, 9, 115, 136, 145
Braybrooke of Billingbere, Lord, 1
Breese T C, 72
Brian P W, 7, 8, 55, 56, [60] 87, 145
Brian R C, 8, 62, 67, 69, 70, 73, [86] 130, [136]
Bridges R C, 66
Brooks D H, 92, 93, [97]
Buckley N G, 94
Bukovac M J, [60]
Bullock D W R, 107, 125
Burnet I M, 37, 38 [41]
Burrage L J, 6
Busvine J R, 145

Calderbank A, [54] 61, 80, [86] 123, 125, [127]
Callan I W M, [34] 110
Carroll T H J, 3, 12

Carson Rachel, 119
Cattlin N, 66
Cavell B D, 123, [127]
Chandler Margaret, 109
Charlton D F, 117
Charlton J L, 61
Charlton Kay, 61
Cheveley S W, 6, 10, 12, 64, 145
Clark J, 26, [28]
Clayton J, 43, 121, 136
Clinch R C, 63, 93
Coggins R E, 57
Cole Ann, 90 [97]
Collier P A, 7
Conning D, 140
Cooke G W, 13
Cooper A, 133
Cotterell R, 16, 79, [86]
Cowan W T, 110
Coyne F P, 57
Cremlyn R J W, 61
Crockford N W R, 121
Cronshey J F H, 63, 112
Cross B E, [60]
Crossman A R
Crowdy S H, 8, 62, 87, 112, [118] 145
Curtis P J, 55

Darter I E, 111, 112
Davey D G, 89
Davies L M, [28]
Day D, 117
Douglas G, 73, 78, [86]
Dowden H G, 96
Downing F S, 46
Doyle P, 9
Drewe N W, 31
Dunning R A, 52
Dupire A, 43

Edgar E C, 51, [54]
Edwards M J, 125, [127]
Edwards P J, 122
Elias R S, 89, 115, [118]
Elson G W, 55, 57
Elsworth J E, [34] 93
Evans D D, 101, 105

Faraday Michael (1825), 42
Farrell G M, 96, [97]
Farrington J A, 66, 70
Ferguson W S, 5, 22, 23, 24
Finney J R, 80, 96, [97]
Fixsen B A, 5
Fleck, Sir Alexander, (Lord Fleck), 64
Floyd A, 61
Fox H M, 31, 83
Freeman P F H, 89, 131
Fryer, Sir John, 36, 37

Gage J C, 50, [54] 122
Gavin, Sir William, 6, 145
Geoghegan M J, 126, 130, 131, [136] 137, 145

Ghosh R, 8, 49, 50, [54] 61, 62, 106
Gilbert J H (Sir Henry Gilbert) 1, 17
Gillard Grace, 105
Godbold E M, 90, 112
Gomeza Ozámiz, J M, 43
Gow J S, [144]
Grabham N, 93
Greenhill A W, 3, 12, [27]
Grove J, [127]
Grove J F, [60]

Hale C J, 105
Hall D W, [97]
Halliday D J, 7, [9] 64
Hamilton R A, 10, 145
Hammond P S, [118]
Harlow Ann, 47, [48] 50, 121
Harnisch S, [144]
Harris D A, 32, [34] 84, 111
Hart C A, 66
Headford D W R, 73, 82, [86]
Hearne Thomas, 1
Heath G W, 121
Hemming H G, 55
Hemingway R J, 123, 124, [127]
Hendley P, 124
Heritage K J, 66
Hield H Z, 57
Hill I R, 126
Holden J S, 146
Holdom R S, 138
Holmes E, 37
Homer R F, 8, 61, 69, [86]
Hood A E M, 13, 14, 16, [27] [28] 79, [86]
Hopf H S, 47, 50, 121
Hussey N W, 109

Jameson H R, 6, 16, 44, 45, 46, [47] [48]
    79, [86] 134, 135, [136]
Jeater R S L, 76, 79, [86]
Jefferies E G, 55
Johnen B G, 126
Jones Martin G, 5, 12, [27] 145
Jones D Price, 40, 63, 64
Jones D Rudd, 62, 145
Jones R L, 67

Kay I T, 99
Keeble Sir Frederick, 2, 3, 4, 22, 147
Keen Sir Bernard, 110
Kellner O, 23
Kinch D, 140, 141
King P P, 137
Kirchgessner M, [144]
Knight B A G, 69, 80
Knight, Kathleen, 126, 131
Kögl F, 35
Koronka P, 84
Krezdorn A H, 57

Lawes J B (Sir John Bennett Lawes), 1, 17
Lawrence D K, 146
Lawrence J C, 117
Leahey J P, 124, [127]

Lean O B, 5, 6
Leatherdale D, 64
Lewis A H, 2, 5, 6, 8, 12, 17, 18
Lewis C J, 78, [86]
Liebig J von, 17
Linden van der, 42
Littlehailes J D, [144]
Low A J, 13, 16, 19, [28] 74, 122, [136]
Lyne P M, 96

McCallum Deighton J, 103, 104, [109]
McCracken A, 101
McHattie V G, 88
McIlvenny H C, 78, [86] 135
McLennan D, 138
McMillan J, 55, [60]
McNaughton E J, 64
Maddison D, 32
Markey R J, 105, 108
Marrs G J, 117
Marth P C, 38, [41]
Martinez A, 108
Masters Joan, 99, 101, 107, 108
Mees G C, 56, 62, 70, [86] 99, 101, 108
Melchett Lord (see Sir Alfred Mond)
Mellor H C, 112
Merrett R, 101
Middleton M R, 33, [34] 101
Milik J F, 33
Mitchell J W, 38, [41] 135
Mitchelson I, 110
Mond, Sir Alfred (Lord Melchett), 2, 37
Morgan Claire, 123, 125, [127]
Morgan D G, 56, 62
Morris E O, 138
Morrod R S, 127, 146
Mulholland T P C, [60]

Newman J F, 46, 47, [48] 50, 121, 122,
    [127]
Newton, Sir Isaac, 67
Nield P, [48]
Nusbaum C J, 135
Nutman P S, 37, [41]

Offield R, 31, 94
Ordish F G, 42, 43, [47]
Oslage H J, [144]
Ousby J, 138
Owen T R, 138

Padwick G Watts, 29, 110, 145
Page H J, 3, 5, 12, 17, 145
Parham M R, 103
Pascoe R, 104
Paté L, 108
Pattison O J, 11
Paul J, 90
Paulin G, 108
Peacock F C, 45, 64, 101, 135, [136] 136
Peacock Mary, 64
Peel Col. W R, 5, 6
Pharis R P, 59
Pickering R, 103

Pike I H, 24
Plowman R E, 116
Preston W H, 135
Price C E, 66
Procter J, 3, 13, [27]
Proctor J H, 101
Pullen J, [109]
Purnell T J, 94

Quastel J R, 37, [41] 130
Quayle J R, 138

Radley Margaret, 55, 56
Raucourt M, 43
Rayns F, 37
Reader W J, 4, [9]
Rhodes D N, [144]
Rickards J, 65
Ridley S M, 146
Riley D, 80, 127
Rivett P R, 101, 105
Robson J, 51
Roesler F C, 139
Roque, 1
Roques J F, 108
Roth F X, [144]
Roy J H B, [144]
Ruscoe C N E, 101

Salter Joan, 64
Sandegren E, 56
Sanderson J F, [118]
Sarney A E, 63
Saunders B C, 49
Schrader G, 7, 49
Schultz E, [144]
Seaman D, 66
Sexton W A, 36, 37, [41] 55, 134
Sharp D G, 84
Sharp F L, 7, 61
Sharpe S P, 98
Shepherd C E, 61, 117
Shephard Claire, 90, [97]
Sherlock E, 31
Silk J A, [54] 61, 65
Sinclair Kathleen, 3
Slade P, 123, [127]
Slade R E, 5, 23, 36, 37, [41] 44, 47, [48] 134
Smart J C, 6
Smith A E, 123, [127]
Smith Diana, 140
Smith S R L, 138, [144]
Snares John, 1
Snell B K, 89, 98
Spencer L G, 40, 52, 56
Speyer F C, 6, 10
Stanley Joan, 65
Stapledon Sir George, 6
Stapley J H, 45, 111, [118]
Steel W O, 121
Stobo I J F, [144]
Stock G H, 42, 43, 121
Stringer D A, 140

Stubbs J, 67, 73, 89
Summers L A, 61, 65, 145
Suter J, 55
Sylvester J B, [9]

Tanner C C, 6, 42, 43, 44, [48] 64
Taylor Jean, 136
Taylor R T, 33, 109
Teal G, 123, [127]
Templeman W G, 5, 6, 8, 13, 36, 37, 38, 39, [41] 55, 132, [136] 145
Thomas F J D, 6, 42, 43, [48]
Thomas Rt. Hon J H, 3
Thompson W, 11
Thornton H G, 37, [41]
Tipler R V, 30, 110, [118]
Tomkins D J, 58
Tomlinson T E, 16, [28] 62, 69, [86]
Torges H G, [144]
Turner A G, 138
Turner B, 123
Turner J A W, 52, 96, [97]
Turner J N, 57, [60] 61
Turner Mary, 96
Turner R R, 11

Uvarov B P, 44

Varley J E, 94
Virtanen A I, 22
Vogt H, [144]

Waitt A W, 127
Wal P van der, [144]
Walker R B, [144]
Walter H, 1823, 1
Warrington R P, 117
Watchorn N, 24, 137, 140
Waterworth D G, 140
Watson S J, (Sir Stephen Watson), 3, 5, 6, 12, 22, 23, 24, [28] 145
Watts R F, 32
Weaver R J, 57
Webley D M, 130
Went F W, 35
Wheeler A F J, 72, 75, 81
White B G, 66
Wilkinson W, 121
Wilson A, 141
Winchester J M, 31, 63, 117
Wittwer S H, [60]
Woodman H E, 22
Woodward R C, 5, 6, [48]
Woolner M, [97]
Wright N, 65, 127
Wünsche W A, [118]

Yuen S H, 125, [127]

Zuckerman Sir Solly, 119, 125